# Collector's Guide To Miniature

# Teddy Bears

## Identification & Values

# Cynthia Powell

**COLLECTOR BOOKS**

*A Division of Schroeder Publishing Co., Inc.*

The current values in this book should be used only as a guide. They are not intended to set prices, which vary from one section of the country to another. Auction prices as well as dealer prices vary greatly and are affected by condition as well as demand. Neither the Author nor the Publisher assumes responsibility for any losses that might be incurred as a result of consulting this guide.

Cover Photo: 3½" (9 cm) white Steiff, c. 'teens, $800.00 up
5" (13 cm) gold Schuco bottle bear, c. 1950's, $600.00 up
3½" (9 cm) blue Schuco, c. 1930's, $700.00 up
2¾" (7 cm) vermilion Schuco, c. 1930's, $250.00 up
3¼" (8 cm) gold Japanese Ted, c. 1930's, $50.00 up
Top right — 2⅜" (6 cm) brown Schuco, c. 1920's, $275.00 up

## *Searching For A Publisher?*

We are always looking for knowledgeable people considered to be experts within their fields. If you feel that there is a real need for a book on your collectible subject and have a large comprehensive collection, contact us.

COLLECTOR BOOKS
P.O. Box 3009
Paducah, Kentucky 42002-3009

Cover design by Sherry Kraus
Book design by Gina Lage

Additional copies of this book may be ordered from:

Collector Books
P.O. Box 3009
Paducah, Kentucky  42002-3009

@ $17.95.  Add $2.00 for postage and handling.

Copyright: Cynthia Powell, 1994

# Dedication

*This book is dedicated to my husband and hero, Gary Cosgrove, whose soul is as strong as a bear, and whose heart is as true as a Teddy Bear.*

# About the Author

**Cynthia Powell**

Cynthia Powell is an award-winning miniature bear artist who has assembled one of the countries finest collections of vintage to modern tiny Teddies. Her work has been featured in several books on Teddy Bears, and photos of her creations appear regularly in collector's publications. She is also an experienced close-up photographer whose miniature bear slide shows have educated and entertained at collector's conventions.

Cynthia earned a Bachelor's degree in Fine Arts from the University of Wyoming and a Graduate Gemologist diploma from the Gemological Institute of America. When Cynthia, her husband, and three cats moved to sunny Orlando in 1989, she traded an eight year career as a jewelry designer, buyer and appraiser to pursue bear-making and writing. She's been beary happy ever since.

# Acknowledgments

Special thanks to my father, Dr. Leon Powell, the best research assistant and proofreader a daughter could have; to my mother, Anne Powell, for teaching me to read with Winnie the Pooh; and to Nanny Lena, the angel sitting on my shoulder. Thanks to Sara and George Phillips, two great friends and bear-buddies who invited me to visit their happy home for many fun "feasts" and Teddy talks. My sincere appreciation to Karen Thompson for her friendship and enthusiasm and for sharing her fine contemporary collection; to Susan Wiley, who graciously accepted me into her "den" to photograph her Teddy bear treasures; to Donna West and Dickie Harrison for a fun and informative photo session at the house; and to Barry Hoffman for bringing the bear! Thanks to Harriet Purtill for her patience and trust; to Barbara Lauver for generously sharing her knowledge; to Carol Porter for sending so many fine bears; to Laurie Sasaki, Cindy Martin, Elaine Gamble and D.A. Horton for posting their antique Teds by mail. My gratitude also goes to Regina Prugh at the Owl and the Pussycat for her continued support; to Leisa Masters for her contagious love of Teddies; to Domenico Idoni for his Schuco enthusiasm; to Kathy George for the photographs; to Mercy Birnn, Barbara Baldwin, Michelle Daunton, David Douglass, and Nancy Torode for their kind cooperation.

Pricing Note: The values in this book reflect information gathered from many sources. Dealers, auction houses, shops, price lists, and collectors all contributed educated opinions. Where estimates varied, an average value was determined. The bear "market" is constantly fluctuating, and prices will differ among regions, buyers and dealers. Many examples shown are one-of-a-kind, and if sold, will bring whatever one collector is willing to pay.

# Table of Contents

Chapter 1:
The Lasting Appeal of Little Bears ...........................................................6

Chapter 2:
Collecting Basics.............................................................................16

Chapter 3:
Miniature Steiff Bears......................................................................26

Chapter 4:
Miniature Schuco Bears ....................................................................41

Chapter 5:
Japanese Miniatures .......................................................................80

Chapter 6:
Miscellaneous Miniatures ..................................................................90

Chapter 7:
Uptown Teddies — Silver, Gold and Other Elegant Bear Accessories................106

Chapter 8:
Contemporary Teddies, Manufactured .............................................115

Chapter 9:
Contemporary Artist Bears................................................................127

Chapter 10:
The Smallest Bear in the World .........................................................154

# Chapter One

# The Lasting Appeal of Little Bears

The bear craze began in the United States around 1906, just a few years after president Theodore Roosevelt's fateful hunting trip to Mississippi. Clifford Berryman's political cartoons, associating the popular president with a cute, Teddy-like cub, inspired toy makers to market their play bears under Roosevelt's widely-known nickname. In the true spirit of American capitalism, the world's most beloved toy was born. (See Plate 1.)

Teddy's popularity spread quickly to Britain and Europe, where the bear frenzy escalated, unchecked, until the onset of World War I. With the historical popularity of the Teddy came a proliferation of bear shapes and sizes too numerous to mention in one volume. Now, nearly a century since the early bear enthusiasm, the world is once again in the midst of "bear mania." (See Plate 2.)

Concurrent with today's collecting craze another bear phenomenon is evident — the yen for miniature Teddies. Diminutive, but desirable, tiny Teds six inches and under are stealing collector's hearts away from their larger bear brothers.

Since the beginning of Teddy Bear history, approximately 1903, miniature bears have been produced in colors ranging from racy red and precious pink to the more mundane shades of brown and gold mohair. They've been manufactured in fabric, metal, glass, wood, porcelain, papier maché,

PLATE 2
Move over Dolly dear, Teddy is here! The unprecedented success of the early Teds had doll makers worried. Would their fragile, unforgiving creations be banned from the playroom, replaced by the more rambunctious bear? In defense they created the Teddy doll, a jointed bear body with a feminine face. But this strange-looking novelty did not catch on. Dolls, after all, do not have fur. The 5" (12.5 cm) example at left, probably American-made, is c. 1908 with a sweet celluloid face, $500.00. The c. 1910 white Steiff bear stands 3½" (9 cm) high, with black glass bead eyes and a brown floss nose and mouth (collar not original). $400.00 up for fair to good condition. Private Collection.

PLATE 1
The true Teddy evolved from a realistic, bruin-styled bear on all fours into the cuddlier, anthropomorphically articulated version we know and love today. The 2½" (6.5 cm) gold bear on the left was made by Emily Farmer in the style of the earliest Teddies, with distressed fabric, elongated arms, large feet and a pronounced hump, $95.00. The 1¾" (4.5 cm) X 2" (5 cm) Bear on Wheels (right) is a more animal-like adaptation, $125.00.

sterling silver, and solid gold. They have lent their therapeutic Teddy charm to hat pins, button-hooks, perfume bottles, pincushions, tape-measures, seals, and cufflinks, inviting a smile wherever they go. (See Plates 3 – 4.)

Nearly a century of kids have chewed, carried, cuddled, and abused them. Though they may have been scaled down for children, adults adored them as well. Flapper women tucked tiny Teddy perfumes and gin-filled bear flasks into their purses during prohibition, and soldiers carried pocket-sized bears bravely into battle. (See Plate 5.)

**PLATE 3**
Miniature bears have been made in nearly every color conceivable. These five fancy-colored Schucos, c. 1927, are more desirable than their beige or brown-toned brothers. Their collectibility is further increased by their near mint condition and the delightful surprises they conceal within their 3½" (9 cm) bodies — mirrored compacts complete with lipstick, powder, and puff. $1,000.00 up for excellent to mint condition. Private Collection.

**PLATE 4**
Miniature bears have been manufactured in materials ranging from gold to plastic. These three are 1½" (4 cm) of papier maché (maker unknown), 4" (10 cm) of pink celluloid from Japan, and 2½" (6.5 cm) of mohair over metal by Schuco. $45.00, $55.00, $275.00.

**PLATE 5**
This 4" (10 cm) mohair bear, possibly British, has a provenance that is priceless. The original owner was a WWI pilot, who carried the little Teddy as a good luck talisman while flying on dangerous missions. The magic must have worked, because the fortunate flyer lived until age 93. Adding to the charm of this treasured Ted is his worn condition (an obvious sign of great bravery and many battles won) and the brown stains on his feet, probably acquired by sharing a favored pocket with some sweet-smelling tobacco. $1,000.00 up. Courtesy D.A. Horton.

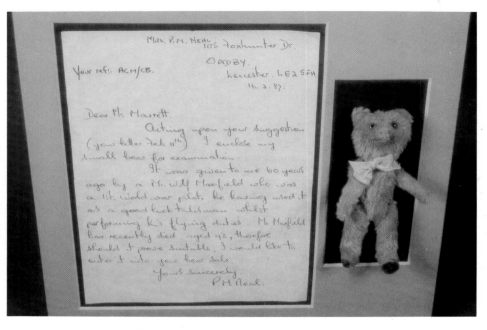

Today's bear collector covets them all. If Teddy Bears are terrific, tiny bears are even better. When living space and budgets seem to be shrinking, miniature bears make more sense than ever. (See Plates 6 – 8.)

Every antique aficionado knows that the prices of vintage bears have gone through the roof. Since the value of these expensive toys is often calculated per inch, many collectors are exercising some semblance of economy by buying smaller bears. Specializing in one area allows the buyer to build a more complete and important collection. Besides, the tinier the Teddies, the more of them we can squeeze into our homes!

Even contemporary artists have jumped on the miniature bear bandwagon by sewing their Teddy Bear fantasies into reality. Small "antique" Teddies are hard to find. So in order to satisfy their insatiable bear cravings, a few creative collectors have learned to make their own. The intricacy, craftsmanship, and imaginative designs of these modern bears often surpass the quality and scarcity of their antique ancestors. (See Plates 9 – 15.)

Old or new, these tiny "jewels" of Teddy beardom combine the fun of toy collecting with the intrinsic value and investment potential of fine gems. Beauty, rarity, portability, provenance, and durability are a few of the factors that these Teddy

**PLATE 6**
**Incredible shrinking pandas! These two Teds by artist Ann Inman show a popular trend in Teddies today — smaller sewing. The 2¾" (7 cm) hand-stitched plush miniature, perfectly reproduced in every detail, perches atop the 12" (30 cm) machine-sewn, mohair version. Large, $150.00; small, $95.00.**

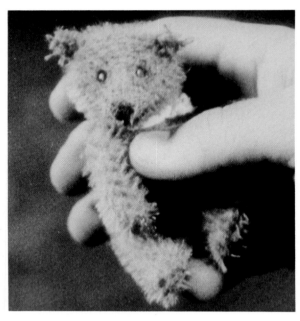

**This mini-bear made it big in Hollywood with a supporting role in the 1927 Paramount Picture, *Wings*. The Ted plays a good luck mascot for WWI fighter pilot, David Armstrong (played by Richard Arlen), in the poignant, Oscar-winning tale of adventure and romance. David keeps his childhood toy in his shirt-pocket, along with a love note and his decoration of honor, but disaster strikes when the bear is left behind. Check it out at your local video store, but have the hankies ready for Ted's final, heart-rending scene. COURTESY OF PARAMOUNT PICTURES. *Wings* Copyright 1993© by Paramount Pictures, All Rights Reserved.**

Bear treasures have in common with precious stones. (See Plate 16.)

Like rubies, emeralds, and sapphires, little bears have their own brand of cuteness or "beauty," which will help hold their value over the years. So remember, miniature Teddies (and diamonds) are your best friends.

Rarity is exemplified when we compare the prices of mini-bears to those of their larger cousins. Teddy Baby, a distinctive Steiff bear made from 1930 through the early 1950's with a velvet snout and velvet feet, is more rare and desirable in the smallest (3½"/9 cm) size, and, consequently, commands a higher price per inch than any of the larger versions.

The durability of bears depends on the craftsmanship of the maker and the care of the owner, but, generally, small bears are deceptively sturdy for their size. What other tiny toys could so nobly withstand the repeated tugs and hugs of a loving child? One particularly brave miniature bear even survived the sinking of the Titanic. His owner, 36 year old Gaspare Gatti, manager of the ship's first class restaurant, was not so lucky. The little bear has found a safer home now at the Ribchester Museum of Childhood in Lancashire, England.

**PLATE 7**
**This 16" (40 cm) Bialosky "Susie" bear, manufactured by Gund, proudly displays a tiny, 2" (5 cm) replica of her-self by artist Carol Stewart. Large, $55.00; small, $200.00.**

Portability plays an important role in today's world where mobility has become a survival skill. Having a hard day at the office? Miniature bears can be cleverly concealed in a pocket or purse for instant stress-relief. Tiny executive Teds prefer to travel in briefcases. (See Plates 17 – 19.)

Of course, this private kind of companionship is half the charm of mini-bear friends. We don't have to share, or show them to anyone. The professional facade we present to society can be left comfortably in place while secret Teddy talisman's come along incognito. (See Plates 20 – 23.)

Like the fetish carvings of the Zuni Indians or the ancient amulets of the Egyptians, little bears are a contemporary version of the magic charm, warding off the accelerated evils of a modern world with the whimsical power of a sewn-on smile. (See Plates 24 – 25.)

In the late twentieth century where technology is evolving faster than humans can adapt to it, where the pace of living is furious and fierce, and cultural and economic pressures often take precedence over friends and family, we need this Teddy Bear magic more than ever. Not as a Freudian escape back to the nursery, but as a very adult reaffirmation of our caring and compassionate side.

Unconditional acceptance, wide-eyed wonder, lasting loyalty, and love are all reflected in the smiling, slightly shaggy gaze of an old bear. And if that bear is small, we can hold a bit of history and hope within our hand, and pass it down for generations to come. (See Plate 26.)

**PLATE 8**
**This 11" (28 cm) "Yetta Nother Bear" is one of the original designs by artist Carol-Lynn Rössel Waugh from which the House of Nisbet in England produced Yetta commercially from 1987 to 1991. "Little Yetta," only 2½" (6.5 cm) tall, wears a miniature, matching outfit and was hand-sewn by Carol-Lynn. $275.00.**

PLATE 10
A green Schuco perfume bottle bear and green good luck bear (doll "charm" inside not original), both 3½" (9 cm), c. 1920's – 1930's, were the motivating idea behind the artist bear pictured below left. Schuco. $1,000.00 up.

PLATE 9
Many modern bear-makers are inspired by the antique. "Torley" is a one of a kind, 5½" (14 cm) distressed mohair bear by Tammie Lawrence with glass eyes, fabric patches and holes purposely placed in his pads to reveal the excelsior stuffing and give him a much-loved look. $280.00.

PLATE 11
Sara Phillips created her own contemporary version of the good luck bear, where the body (a gold-leafed walnut) opens to reveal charms of fortune or happiness. The original Schuco versions contained pigs, elephants, or dolls, but Sara substituted found objects which had more personal significance. $160.00.

PLATE 12
This 3" (7.5 cm) enchanting Merlin bear by Laurie Sasaki takes miniature Teddy creation into a mythical realm never imagined by early bear makers. He is hand-stitched of plush fabric, costumed in several shades of silver and crystal-trimmed synthetic suede, and accessorized with a mysterious wizard's staff. Perfect for casting spells of mini-bear magic. $300.00.

**PLATE 13**
A Teddy Bear garden by artist Octavia Chin sprouts these 3¾" (9.5 cm) fantasy flower bears of green "stem"-colored plush and painted silk petals. Atop each head a bit of pollen is embroidered and a ladybug, bee, or butterfly awaits on the outstretched paws. The ultimate bear bouquet. $110.00 each. Private Collection.

**PLATE 14**
This Teddy comes complete with his own collection. Artist Sara Phillips gathered tiny vintage charms to accessorize her 2¼" (5.5 cm) cream mohair bear, the centerpiece treasure in a golden metal basket of toy tokens. $175.00.

**PLATE 15**
History-making miniatures. These 2½" (6.5 cm) contemporary Teddies were made by Laurie Sasaki (lower left) and Odette Conley (upper right) in the late eighties after a pair of full-sized Steiff muzzle bears set a world record price at auction. Sasaki, $150.00; Conley, $125.00.

**PLATE 16**
Tiny Teds like these 1¼" (3 cm) blue and red perfume and compact bears from Twinklepaws can be as colorful and rare as rubies and sapphires. $245.00 each. Some little bears are made of precious metals like the two older charms at lower left which were cast in low karat gold. $50.00 – 75.00 each.

**PLATE 17**
These 3½" (9 cm) Schuco Bears ride comfortably in the pockets of a business briefcase. The top two are "Janus" bears with double faces that can be swiveled around depending on your morale. Is the boss in a bad mood again? The bear at top left with his bulging eyes and red plastic tongue might express your own response perfectly. Loyal employees carry Teds like the Blue Schuco at lower right, dressed in their favorite corporate color. $700.00 up. Private Collection.

**PLATE 18**
A 3¼" (8 cm) Japanese bear, c. 1930, surveys the world from the safety of a pocket. Please tuck his head down in case of rain. $40.00.

**PLATE 19**
Tammie Lawrence's 5½" (14 cm) "Lillybeth" bear fits inside her own vintage leather purse for traveling. "Antiqued" to match the period of her handbag, this bear has glass eyes, leaking excelsior stuffing and a jewel and flower-bedecked dress designed from an old silk handkerchief. $350.00.

**PLATE 20**
"Travel Teddy," 1¾" (4.5 cm), by Sara Phillips, comes with a miniature trunk handmade by the artist, complete with exotic labels from far away places. This bear's clothes, muff and cape, all made from vintage trims, are completely removable and can be stored inside with a matching hat and a minute bottle of "eau de Honey" perfume. Now, that's traveling in style! $325.00.

**PLATE 21**
With a wistful face that's sure to get a handsome tip, this 3¼"
(8 cm) bellhop bear by artist Dickie Harrison carries a coordinating plaid suitcase. $150.00.

**PLATE 22**
Little bears often have little boxes as an integral part of their
design, adding to the delight of owning one. Kimberlee Port's
2" (5 cm) Jester Muff, dressed in pink and maroon, can be easily transported in his handmade gift box of marbled paper.
$350.00. Private Collection.

**PLATE 23**
"Benjamin Bear," a 1¾" (4.5 cm) gold Teddy by British artist Anita Oliver sits atop a Marx
metal trunk that's just his size. Anita's 1¼" (4 cm) "Oliver" bear arrives in a handcrafted,
custom-fitted box. $90.00 – 100.00.

**PLATE 24**
Long before miniature Teddies came into being, the bear was a symbol of strength and power, condensed here in the shape of an amulet. This 1" high Zuni fetish bear is a contemporary carving of turquoise trimmed with stones and feathers. $50.00. Courtesy Donna Harrison West.

**PLATE 25**
Beth Hogan's 3¼" (8 cm) multicolored Jester Bear bestows a bit of modern Teddy magic with his sparkling crystal wand — a contemporary talisman sure to protect his beloved owner. $125.00. Courtesy Karen Thompson.

**PLATE 26**
Handling a 5" (12.5 cm) Schuco perfume bottle bear, c. 1920's – 1930's, is a special experience when you consider how one little bear is a combination of art, ingenuity, and invention all sewn up into a fun, fuzzy bundle. This particular Teddy, a gift from my father, will always hold extra meaning for me. $600.00 up in excellent to mint condition.

# Chapter Two

# Collecting Basics

Teddy collecting may not seem like the perfect pastime for thrill-seekers, but few pursuits can produce a rush of excitement like finding a forgotten bear partially buried beneath the clutter on an antique dealer's table. If the bear is an especially rare example with a two dollar price tag attached, the delight is even greater.

Has this ever happened to me? No! But it's the anticipation that keeps the dedicated (or should I say addicted?) collector searching. You never know what marvelous bears may be waiting for you to find them.

In this way, bear collecting is a bit like treasure hunting. Tiny Teddy riches could lie just inside the next shop, or the bear cache may be clearly marked for you on a dealer's price list or auction catalog, leading the way like a map to the buried treasure. The risks may not be as dangerous, but the rewards can be just as great!

Mini-bear collectors may not be moved by the dull glint of a golden coin, but tell them you've spotted a pink Schuco perfume bottle bear, mint in its original box, and the chase is on. Unfortunately, such fabulous finds are few and far between. A Teddy Bear hunter must be patient.

Where then should you start your search? First, check the resource guide at the back of this book. It lists a number of dealers, magazines, museums, stores, clubs and catalogs that can help direct you to the small bear of your dreams.

You might continue the hunt in your own neighborhood. I've heard of several tantalizing treasures turning up at garage or estate sales, although I often wonder if these stories are merely wishful fantasies. You are more likely to find a lot of non-bear "bargains" such as toasters or vacuum cleaners. These are definitely not items you need like little bears.

If you're shopping for newer miniatures and artist bears, there are a number of stores that specialize in this area, and when you're just starting to buy, a knowledgeable shop owner or employee may offer valuable advice and help you refine your wish list. With their assistance or with the help of your favorite antique Teddy dealer you can plan your collection.

Remember, there is a difference between a true collection and a mere accumulation. Haphazard spending may give immediate gratification, but a few years down the road, when your taste and budget changes, you may regret those early purchases. Invest some time and effort in studying bears for sale. Check their quality and style, then trust your own instincts.

After a while you'll learn to focus on the bears that appeal to you. Defining your collection by a theme or specialty may be appropriate depending on your taste or budget. If your pocketbook is shallow, price may be a significant factor, but no matter what your spending range is, try to opt for quality over quantity. You can never go wrong by buying the best. (See Plates 27 – 29.)

Many factors affect the value of "antique" or vintage bears, and you should keep these in mind when considering an important purchase. Condition, rarity, desirability, provenance, color, and "cuteness" are all elements to weigh before you buy a vintage bear.

Condition can be a relative term depending on the person you ask. Words like Mint, Excellent, Very Good or Good may be used with greater frequency and less accuracy than Webster would allow. "Well-loved" is a favorite euphemism for a Teddy in worn condition (the bear business equivalent of the romantic real estate phrase "fixer upper.")

**PLATE 27**
Any good, well thought out collection will have an underlying theme to it. The miniature bear category is already a theme in itself, but this all-white grouping takes the idea one step further. The 9" plush Gund bear at the rear is not a miniature, but makes a good backdrop for the other bears. From left to right, a 2⅜" (6 cm) early Schuco, a 2¾" (7 cm) later model Schuco, a ¾" (2 cm) Tiggy Winkle, a 1½" (4 cm) German bisque bear, a 7" (18 cm) perfume bottle bear by Mary Kaye Lee, matching 1½" (4 cm) open-mouthed bears by Sara Phillips, and a 1½" (4 cm) Teddy by Anita Oliver. $25.00 – $300.00.

PLATE 28
Pandamonium! Searching for additions to this group might start you dreaming in black and white. The tiniest Ted is at back row, left, a mere ¾" (2cm) from Twinklepaws, next an Austrian chenille-type Teddy 1" (2 cm), Cindy Martin's 5¼" (13.5 cm) Small Panda Yesterbear in mohair, and a 3½" (9 cm) Schuco. At front row, left, is a 2½" (6.5 cm) Panda by Barbara Conley, a 1¾" (4 cm) version by Carol Stewart and a 1⅝" (4 cm) interpretation by Laurie Sasaki. $10.00 – $250.00.

PLATE 29
These 5" (12.5 cm) Schucos, c. 1925 – 1950, may appear different on the outside, but each bear's head can be removed to reveal a perfume bottle inside. $700.00 – $1,100.00 up for each in excellent to mint condition. Private Collection.

17

Of course, there is a great deal of charm attached to a bear that has been hugged to bits by an adoring owner. Some collectors prefer to buy their Teddies in tattered and torn condition. Just be aware that bears in better shape, with all of their mohair present and preferably unfaded, generally bring higher prices and tend to appreciate faster. (See Plates 30 – 31.)

Rarity relates to the relative scarcity of the bear in question. If the style is common, and turns up on dealer's tables with great frequency, it will be less valuable than a Teddy that was produced (or survived) in smaller quantities. But no matter how rare the example, prices will remain low unless the Ted has a high desirability.

The popularity of a particular style, or how desirable it is to collectors, can greatly affect its value. An "ugly" bear, lacking any charm whatsoever, will never bring a high price no matter how rare. Beauty, of course, is in the eye of the beholder, but if the general consensus about a bear's style is low, the desirability suffers. (See Plates 32 – 33.)

The provenance, or known history of an item, can be a significant factor affecting its value. Especially when that item is a Teddy Bear. Teddy aficionados often buy for love alone, and few other purchases are as emotionally charged.

A story associated with a particular Teddy may evoke bits of history or memories of the past. Through the bear we can share the joys and sorrows of people now gone. Teddy's presence is our reassuring link to their ephemeral lives.

**PLATE 30**
It's a cat, it's a bear, it's...? We may never know the true identity of this 3¼" (8 cm) over-cuddled creature by British toymaker Alpha Farnell, but it's cute whatever it is, and someone obviously loved it very much. In this case, condition creates extra charisma. $100.00. Courtesy Cindy Martin.

**PLATE 31**
This 5½" (14 cm) Gold Schuco tumbler with original box, still sporting his green satin scarf and "Made in Germany" body tag, is a fine example of a bear in mint condition. $800.00 up with box. Private Collection.

**PLATE 32**
These 3½" (9 cm) tan Schucos from
the early seventies were dressed
especially for the Enchanted Doll-
house in Manchester, Vermont.
Here, the special clothing makes
the basic colored bears more rare.
$400.00 for the pair. Private Collec-
tion.

**PLATE 33**
Teddy Baby from Steiff is a universal favorite among collectors
and considered to be a very desirable bear. This 3½" (9 cm) example has a "Made in U.S. Zone Germany" ribbon sewn into his arm
seam, making him even more interesting and establishing his age
between 1948 and 1953. $1,600.00 up. Private Collection.

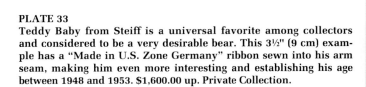

**PLATE 34**
This 3½" (9 cm) Schuco compact bear brings back memories for its owner, Merci Birnn. After admiring the little Teddy at an older girlfriend's house, the girl presented it to Merci as a gift, explaining that the miniature bears had been favors at her sweet 16 celebration. Now that's what I call a party! $500.00 up in fair to good condition.

A 3½" (9 cm) Schuco compact in basic gold is a desirable bear. But if the owner of a particular compact remembers how the little Teddies were given as favors at her friend's sweet 16 party, the delightful account adds appeal to the bear. (See Plates 34 – 35.)

A well-documented background with a famous or interesting owner can also lend value. "Alfonzo," currently owned by Ian Pout, is "an exceptionally rare, red Steiff bear originally bought in 1908 for Princess Xenia Georgievna by her father, the Grand Duke of Russia." Such a provenance gives that Teddy a romantic history. (See Plate 36.)

Color too, can significantly impact value. Basic bear tones like gold, tan and brown are usually the most common and consequently not as rare or expensive as some of the wilder, scarcer shades. Fancy-colored Schucos can be twice as costly as their plain gold brothers. Few white or cream bears have survived unsoiled and are highly sought after today. Black bears, even in miniature, are also quite rare. (See Plate 37.)

"Cuteness" is the last, and possibly most important factor to consider when selecting a bear. Ultimately, the decision to buy or not to buy may depend on Teddy's expression. Harried sales clerks may not always understand why you have to inspect each seemingly identical Teddy on their shelf, but true bear lovers know that every bear was not created equal. With all other factors being the same, a seductively sweet face will be adopted first, and in the case of older bears, usually for a higher price. (See Plate 38.)

Although preference for a certain Ted may be very personal, some bears definitely elicit more wistful sighs than others. If you're ever in doubt, remember to follow your heart. Is he winsome, wise, or simply irresistible? Are those little bear lips secretly whispering "Take me home"? Congratulations, you've just adopted a friend for life.

So what happens when you get him home? Here the advantage of miniature bears over bigger Teddies becomes happily apparent. More than one

**PLATE 35**
Here the c. 1930's compact is opened to reveal the powder, puff, and red lipstick still intact.
Courtesy Merci Birnn.

**PLATE 36**
"Alfonzo" is 1⅞" (4.5 cm) after shrinking! Ian Pout had Steiff reproduce this treasured bear in full size, but for small bear collectors, this miniature cast version by Colour Box, limited to two thousand, is available from Teddy Bears of Whitney in England. $20.00.

**PLATE 37**
This 2⅜" (6 cm) Schuco, c. 1925 – 1930, was made in rare black mohair with matching black felt paw pads. Historically, black bears have not been great sellers for the companies that produced them, so fewer were made, enhancing their current collectibility. $300.00. Courtesy Harriet Purtill.

**PLATE 38**
Hug me! This 5" (13 cm) Steiff rattle bear, c. 1925, has an exceptionally expressive face that only the coolest of collectors could resist. Most of his mohair has been rubbed away, but it has only added to his cuteness. Vintage flower trim not original. $500.00 up for fair condition. Private Collection.

closet collector has secreted a baby bruin home via purse or pocket, carefully hidden from the watchful eyes of a skeptical spouse. Many fine little bear collections have been built this way, and if you are not blessed as I am with an exceptionally indulgent husband, I heartily endorse this clandestine method of collecting.

Once he's safely residing (or hidden) at home, Teddy may need to be cleaned, aired, or repaired. Go easy, though, because if you have no experience in this area, you may aggravate rather than ameliorate Ted's affliction.

Unraveling seams or gaping holes can be closed with a simple ladder stitch to prevent stuffing loss. Knowledgeable restorers frequently suggest vacuuming an old bear to remove dust and other potentially damaging dirt, but the vacuum cleaner can't distinguish between a little bear and a large ball of fur. If Ted's unwittingly ingested down the tube, you might have a hard time finding each other again. Don't forget to cover the hole with cheesecloth, or try dusting your bear off with a clean, soft toothbrush instead.

I do not recommend trying to bathe an old bear by yourself. This delicate job is better left to professional dealers or bear "doctors" who are properly equipped to avoid the potential dangers of water spots, color bleeding, shrinking, or fading fabric. If you do attempt any bear repairs, make sure that whatever you do can be undone later. When in doubt, leave Ted in his original condition. (See Plates 39 – 40.)

**PLATE 39**
**Teddy receives a head transplant! To give you an idea of what a clever seamstress can do, this 3½" "assembled" Schuco bear was found as a lavender body without a head. Ouch! Sara Phillips, an experienced miniature bear artist, kindly rescued him from the unfortunate situation by sewing on a spare head originally intended as a brooch. The ribbon ruff was added to give the mismatched body a costume effect. $150.00.**

**PLATE 40**
**Sew easy, Guys! Two 3½" (9 cm) Steiff Original Teddies in gold and taupe lend a helping paw to a light gold, 2¾" (7 cm) Schuco. Steiffs, $200.00 – $225.00; Schuco, $150.00. Private Collection.**

Displaying your treasures can be one of the great joys of collecting. Here is a chance to give your tiny Teds the privileged environment they deserve. Doll-houses, cabinets, cupboards, and teacups are all possibilities for perfect homes. (See Plates 41 – 49.)

Whatever you use, try to encase your collection behind glass and away from direct sunlight. Dust and fading are two potential problems best avoided. Cedar balls, tansy, or insect-repelling pot-pourri stored inside the same space will help to discourage any small, uninvited visitors.

Keeping a photographic record of your bears is essential for insurance purposes. A written description and thorough documentation of each item will also help you remember where, when and for what price each bear was purchased. This information should be stored in a secure area away from your home. (See Plate 50.)

Should you ever decide to sell or donate your Teds, a complete record could also prove invaluable. A future bear collector, maybe one that isn't even born yet, may use your registry and photos to establish a bear's provenance. Who knows? Some day your favorite bears may be more collectible, because they were owned by you!

**PLATE 41**
A 3½" (9 cm) cream Teddy Baby, c. 1950's, lives a life of pampered luxury in his custom-designed, book-shaped "trunk." Inspired by her admiration for old bears found in their wardrobe and accessory-filled trunks, Sara Phillips decided to outfit her favorite little bear in the same way. A collection of perfectly fitting clothes, shoes, and accessories, all lovingly accumulated, makes a completely charming display. Hats, roller skates, pocketbooks, and trunks are all part of this sweetly spoiled bear's tiny "trousseau." Bear and accessories $2,000.00.

**PLATE 42**
This 3½" (9 cm) brown Teddy Baby, c. 1950's, is perfectly at home in his "Wee Trees" music box tree stump by Joan Wheatley. Delightfully decorated by owner Sara Phillips, the "house" contains everything a rare bear could desire from nutshell baskets to a handmade quilt. A framed postage stamp on the right wall lends the finishing Teddy Bear touch. Bear, $1,200.00; house, $250.00.

**PLATE 43**
Miniature bear artist Janie Comito shows her Teddies in high Victorian style on the brim of a vintage, feather-trimmed hat. The quaintly-clothed bears vary from 4½" (11.5 cm) ladies in high-buttoned shoes to 2½" (6.5 cm) fur-winged angels. $2,725.00 complete. Private Collection.

**PLATE 44**
This doll-house sized Teddy Toy Shop and Salon was designed by artist Cynthia Powell as a fantasy display for her hand-sewn miniature bears and bunnies. A 3" (7.5 cm) Teddy shop owner sells bear wares from tiny ¾" (2 cm) synthetic suede Teddies to custom bear watercolor paintings. Individual bears $150.00 up. Private Collection.

**PLATE 45**
The front window looking into the shop shows a 2" (5 cm) pink Teddy with golden paw pads riding a 1¾" (4.5 cm) high, jewel-collared cat on wheels. $500.00.

**PLATE 46**
Little bears will fit nearly anywhere. A box of lace makes the perfect hideout for these 2½" (6.5 cm) antique-type Teddies of vintage plush fabric by artist Diane Turbarg. $80.00 each.

**PLATE 47**
Bears visit the beach. "Michelle" (Ms. Shell), a 3" (7.5 cm) mer-bear by Karen Marhefka sunbathes on her open clam shell with a ¾" (2 cm) crocheted mermaid-bear by Maggie Anderson and a Bermuda-pink, 2¼" (5.5 cm), shell-trimmed Teddy by April Whitcomb, made for friends to commemorate their vacation at the Pink Beach Club. $150.00, $25.00, and $200.00.

**PLATE 48**
This creative Christmas display by an unknown "interior decorator" was purchased with all items intact by a private collector. The 3¾" (9.5 cm) 1940's white Steiff helps a 2¾" (7 cm) light brown Schuco hang an ornament while a 3½" (9 cm) caramel-colored 1950's Steiff strings garland. $1,000.00.

**PLATE 49**
Teacups and dried French flowers make an effective shelf display for these Teddy treasures, a 1¾" (4.5 cm) dressed girl bear by Carol Stewart, a 2¼" (5.5 cm) pink mohair atomizer bear from Twinklepaws and a 2¾" (7 cm) mohair Ted in a portable lace pocket by Elaine Fujita-Gamble. $90.00 – $225.00.

**PLATE 50**
A 2½" (6.5 cm) tall British guardsman bear by Sandy Williams, protects a 1" (2.5 cm) mini-volume by miniature book publisher, Barbara Raheb. The tiny, leather-bound book contains autographs collected from miniature bear makers, an extra "little" bit of documentation. Bear, $150.00; book, $25.00.

25

# Chapter Three

# Miniature Steiff Bears

Several volumes have been devoted exclusively to Steiff products and to the well-documented history of the world-renowned German toy manufacturer, but let's take a closer look from the perspective of tiny Teddies. Since this book explores the world of miniature bears, it is significant to note that the wildly successful Steiff company started with the making of one miniature animal — a 5" felt elephant.

In 1880 Margaret Steiff, a wheelchair-bound polio survivor, used left-over scraps from her felt dressmaking factory to sew a small elephant pincushion from a pattern found in "Modenwelt" fashion magazine. More pincushions followed; some were given as gifts to Margaret's many nieces and nephews, and some were sold. What started as a stuffed-animal sideline for the felt factory eventually grew into the classic toy company that is still thriving today.

Steiff's first miniature bears were made in 1909. They were fully jointed, machine-sewn, and excelsior stuffed. A tiny Steiff button with an identifying ear-tag was placed in the left ear. The number listed on this tag was 5307 for the smallest bears, "5" for jointed bears, "3" for mohair bears, and "07" referring to the seated height in centimeters. After 1933 or 1934, Steiff began measuring them in a standing position, and the number was changed to 5310, or 10 cm standing (measured with the ears.) (See Plates 51 – 52.)

**PLATE 51**
**This mint condition, 3½" (9 cm) Steiff Teddy, c. 1910, is meticulously made of long, dark gold mohair with black glass bead eyes, a black floss nose and an FF underscored button in the ear (ribbon not original). Note the flat forehead and ears set wide on the head indicating one of the earliest miniatures. $750.00 up. Courtesy Barbara Lauver.**

**PLATE 52**
**White bears are considered rare and desirable, and this 3½" (9 cm) Steiff from the teen's is an exceptionally fine example. The ear button is missing, otherwise Teddy is mint and untouched. Black glass button-shaped eyes and a brown floss nose give the darling little bear an especially sweet expression. $800.00 up. Private Collection.**

The sizes do seem to differ somewhat among individual bears, but this is most likely due to variations in sewing, jointing, and stuffing. Most of the minis fall between 3½" (9 cm) – 3¾" (9.5 cm), but, technically, anything up to 4" (10) cm is cut from the same pattern and is numerically the same bear.

Steiff's basic miniature bear changed gradually over the years and grew easier to manufacture as production costs rose. Labor, rather than materials, became the greatest expense when making miniatures; so in order to supply a realistically priced product, changes were made with time conservation as well as style in mind.

Early bears were made of long mohair, usually in shades of gold, brown and white, with the ears set far apart on the head, glass "bead" or button-shaped eyes, and horizontally stitched floss noses. The older models are also characterized by long, thin, almost pointed feet (without paw-pads or claws), narrow arms, leaner bodies, and small, triangular-shaped heads with low, flat foreheads.

In later Teddies, the ears moved progressively closer together, the foreheads grew higher, the bodies became fatter, and the limbs became a bit less narrow. Nearly every part of the bear filled out or grew more rounded. An educated guess can usually be made about the age by carefully studying these features. (See Plates 53 – 54.)

Additionally, even if the bear has no identification, which happens with a high degree of frequency, it can easily be distinguished as a Steiff by an experienced collector. The seams were closed by hand-sewing in the bear's stomach area and at the top of the arms and legs, close to where the joints were inserted. Ears were sewn directly onto the head rather than being inserted into the seams. There is a certain "look" about Steiff miniatures. The company's high standards of quality sets its bears apart from all other bears. (See Plates 55 – 64.)

After 1965 the glass eyes changed to plastic, a new three-piece pattern replaced the arms, legs, and body, and a bendable wire armature was used instead of joints. The swivel head remained, but tiny jointed bears had become too expensive to manufacture in the traditional manner. (See Plates 65 – 66.)

**PLATE 53**
These five Steiff miniatures, all in the smallest (4"/10 cm) size, are lined up according to age so the progression of pattern and sewing changes can be compared. The bear at far left is the oldest, c. 1910 – 1915, with wide-set, "pointed" features. The bear at far right was made after the switch to a bendable, unjointed body, c. 1965. The bears in between, from approximately 1930 to 1950, grew progressively plumper. $100.00 – $400.00. Private Collection.

**PLATE 54**
Three Steiff bears, 3½" – 4" (9-10 cm), paddle off to a picnic in their own canoe. The oldest, c. 1910, (far right) plays captain to his younger friends from the 1920's (left) and 1930's (center). $400.00 – $750.00 up. Private Collection.

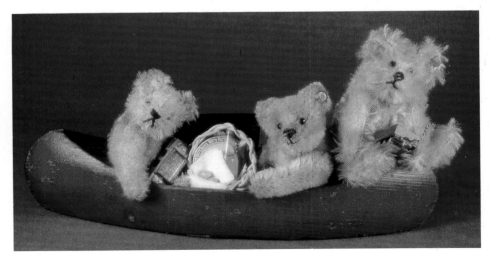

**PLATE 55**
These two 3¾" (9.5 cm) white Steiffs from the 1930's have a poignant tale to tell. They originally belonged to a brother and sister who received them while still children. The two Teddies remained together through the years, carefully kept in pristine condition under a small glass dome. When the owners reached their sixties, the brother became ill, requiring costly nursing care. The sister had to sell both bears to raise money for her brother, but she would only part with the treasured Teds under one condition — they had to be sold as a pair — the bear brother and sister must not be parted. Today they reside comfortably in a private collection, bear buddies forever. $1,200.00 up for the pair.

**PLATE 56**
The ribbon in this bear's arm (not visible in photo) marked "U.S. Zone," dates the 4" (10 cm) Teddy between 1949 and 1953. Other details of this mint condition bear include black glass button-shaped eyes, a black floss nose and script button. $375.00. Private Collection.

**PLATE 57**
This 3¾" (9.5 cm) caramel-colored Steiff has the U.S. Zone ribbon showing in his right arm. Note the style variation between this and the previous bear, even though both can be conclusively dated from the same era. Two bears of the same kind may not look exactly the same. $375.00. Private Collection.

**PLATE 58**
These three Steiff's from the 1950's measure 3½" (9 cm). The Gold Teddy at the left has a raised script button, and the center bear, in a desirable chocolate brown color, was used as an advertising bear with the word "Pertussin" written across his paper chest banner. $200.00 – 375.00. Private Collection.

**PLATE 59**
The 1950's was a prolific and popular era for Steiff products and collectors. These three miniatures, 3½" (9 cm), date from that decade and still retain their "Original Teddy" chest tags and raised script buttons. $325.00 – $375.00 each. Private Collection.

**PLATE 60**
This 1950's miniature, 3¾" (9.5 cm), is only in average shape, but a Steiff in any condition will always be collectible. Some bear lovers prefer to buy a Teddy that can be handled without worry. When purchasing a mint piece there is usually an obligation to keep it perfect and untouched. $175.00. Private Collection.

**PLATE 61**
This 1950's gold Original Teddy, 3½" (9 cm) has a particularly precious, Pooh-like face. Remember, every bear is an individual. Which one speaks to you? $250.00. Private Collection.

**PLATE 62**
Watch out for my nose! This 1950's caramel Steiff, 3½" (9 cm) is mint except for his missing I.D., and a funny floss nose that's been kissed once too often. $200.00. Private Collection.

**PLATE 63**
This perky caramel-colored cub, 4" (10 cm), has bright black, button-shaped, glass eyes and a raised script Steiff button that helps date him from the 1950's to early 1960's. $250.00. Private Collection.

**PLATE 64**
This 3½" (9 cm) sleepy-looking white Steiff from the 1950's has lost his I.D. but not his charm. $175.00. Private Collection.

**PLATE 65**
This 3" (7.5 cm) Panda, from the late sixties to early seventies, has plastic eyes, and the flat, bendable body introduced in 1964. An original box adds to his collectibility. $225.00. Courtesy Merci Birnn.

**PLATE 66**
Comparing this early eighties bendable Original Teddybär with the previous picture shows little change in style over twenty years. The "bendy" bear filled a needed niche in the Steiff line but cannot compare to the classic beauty and craftsmanship of the company's early miniatures. The 2½" (6.5 cm) red velvet elephant is by an unknown maker, probably from the 1930's. Bear, $75.00; elephant, $25.00.

The other basic Steiff Teddy, which can be classified as a miniature, was identified as number 5310 before 1933 – 34 and number 5315 afterward. This bear was 15 cm, or just under 6" high, with black or black and brown glass eyes and was still made without the paw-pads or claws, which show up on larger Steiff bears. Here, too, individual sizes vary somewhat. A crib-toy version of this bear was also made with a melodious rattle hidden inside the body. (See Plates 67 – 71.)

Steiff miniature bears on all fours, c. 1926, were made in a polar bear style with an elongated neck as well as a standard bear version (#1308 02). Both came with a colored mohair collar and bell around the neck and could be purchased separately as individual toys or ornaments, or combined to make the Galop-Teddy motion toy on "eccentric" wheels.

The Roly-Droly, from the same era, was another Steiff toy on wooden wheels to utilize little bears in its design. As a child dragged it along by a string, the 4" (10 cm) Teddies spun merrily behind. It was named for its amusing or droll movement. Record-Teddy, also came in a miniature, 6" (15 cm) size and made a sort of rowing motion when pulled by its eccentric-wheeled cart. (See Plates 72 – 77.)

Teddy Baby, one of Steiff's best-loved bears, was available in miniature from approximately 1930 into the late 1950's. Of the miniature examples I have seen with ear-tags intact, the model number is 7309, or 9 cm (3½"). A 6" or 15 cm size was also made, but proves to be even more elusive. As with all Steiff minis, differences in jointing, sewing and stuffing all led to variations in size, even when the same pattern was used. Sizes may deviate by as much as an inch. (See Plates 78 – 81.)

A miniature Teddyli, #12/712 from the 1950's, came in the style of a dressed doll-bear with a Teddy Baby head. The rubber/latex hands and feet have not worn well over the years because of a tendency to crack. (See Plate 82.)

In the 1950's a 6" jointed Panda with an open mouth became available, as well as a 5" Panda on all fours, #12P/1312,0, and a 5" Koala, #12K/4312. (See Plates 83 – 85.)

The 1980's ushered in new items and contemporary versions of old favorites. Wearable bears seemed to be custom-designed with miniature lovers in mind. Mohair Teddy-head pins came in four collectible colors, a gold-plated bear brooch commemorated the eightieth anniversary of the Teddy Bear (1983), and a ¾" (2 cm) pendant was cast in the form of a fully-jointed metal bear.

My personal favorite, item #8505/01, is surely the smallest bear Steiff ever made. Dangling from a pair of simple chain-style earrings, two tiny Teddies, just ½" (1.5 cm) high, are perfect in every delicate detail, from their jointed arms and legs right down to the microscopic tag and button in each left ear. (See Plates 86 – 91.)

**PLATE 67**
**An FF underscored button with the remnant of a white tag remain in the ear of this 5¼" (13.5 cm) white Steiff, dating the Teddy somewhere between 1911 and 1926. Long, luxurious mohair, brown glass eyes with black pupils, and a brown floss nose give this beautiful bear a very expressive face. $750.00. (The blue ribbon was added recently.) Courtesy Barbara Lauver.**

**PLATE 68**
A slightly shorter mohair gives these 5½" (14 cm) white (FF underscored button in ear) and gold Steiff bears from the 'teens a different look from their fluffier bear friends. Even though this bear pair is fairly well matched in age and style, note the differences in head size and body height. $600.00 – $700.00 each. Private Collection.

**PLATE 69**
Decked out in festive Christmas trim (not original), this 5" (13 cm) Teddy of long gold mohair, c. 1920's, has a black floss nose and Steiff's characteristic brown and black glass eyes. $500.00. Private Collection.

**PLATE 70**
These 6" (15 cm) Steiff rattle bears from the early twenties are rare, and in this case, the taupe or caramel color is the more unusual of the two. The ribbons are not original, but an FF underscored button remains in each left ear. When the bears are shaken, a sweet-sounding bell, or rattle gives the Teddies a chance to "talk." $1,200.00 – $1,500.00 each. Private Collection.

**PLATE 71**
This 5¼" (13.5 cm) rattle Teddy is a bear-collector's dream with its long, lush mohair in near-perfect, pristine condition. The brown floss nose and mouth and brown and black Steiff eyes give Teddy a marvelous Mona Lisa smile. $1,600.00 up. Private Collection.

**PLATE 72**
This very rare Steiff bear on all fours, 2¾" X 4" (7 cm X 10 cm) was available in the mid to late 1920's. The brown glass eyes have black pupils, and a blue mohair ruff (originally with a bell) encircles his neck. $1,500.00 up. Private Collection.

**PLATE 73**
The bear on all fours also came in this slightly longer 2¾" X 4½" (7 cm X 11.5 cm) polar bear version with green mohair neck ruff. $1,500.00 up. Private Collection.

**PLATE 74**
This Roly-Droly toy, from the mid to late 1920's, carried two 4" (10 cm) Teddies in white and gold which spun in opposite directions on their painted wood bases when pulled along by a string. The white bear still wears a red tag (used from approximately 1925 – 1935). This item is very rare, especially in such superb condition. $5,000.00 – $6,000.00 up. Private Collection.

**PLATE 75**
Galop-Teddy, c. 1926 – 1929, sported two of the previously described teddies (also available in gold tones as shown above) on an eccentric-wheeled pull-toy that propelled the bears forward and backward along the metal wires to produce a "galloping" motion. Rare. $4,000.00 – $4,500.00 up. Private Collection.

**PLATE 76**
Galop-Teddy is shown here from another angle. The "polar bear" pattern obviously came in colors other than white.

**PLATE 77**
Record-Teddy, available from 1913, is shown here in the smallest size Steiff made. This little bear, c. 1930, is 4" (10 cm) seated and moves merrily along on his eccentric wheeled cart, rocking back and forth as he goes. Rare. $3,500.00 up. Private Collection.

**PLATE 78**
This 3½" blond Teddy Baby from the 1950's is in tissue — mint condition with his original chest and ear-tags crisp and totally intact. The airbrushed velvet snout and cardboard-reinforced feet are equally clean and perfect. Miniature Teddy Babies are highly sought after, but an example as fine as this one does not come along too often and should raise the adrenalin of even the most advanced collector. $1,800.00 up. Note: fair to good condition Teddy Babies are still available for under $1,000.00. Private Collection.

**PLATE 79**
A divine and darling little bear, this Teddy Baby is super-small, just 3" (7.5 cm) in height, and is probably an early example from the 1930's. The I.D. is missing and the ribbon is not original, but this Teddy has a face to make you fall in love. $1,500.00 up. Private Collection.

**PLATE 80**
This 3½" (9 cm) Teddy Baby, c. 1950's, is made of chocolate brown mohair (the more common of the two miniature colors) with a cream velvet face and feet, brown eyes with black pupils, and a black floss nose. The collar was made by the current owner to match the style found on larger versions. $1,200.00. Courtesy Sara Phillips.

**PLATE 81**
An unusual Teddy Baby, this bear measures 6"
(15 cm) tall and is considered rare due to its
scarce size. The FF underscored button gives an
extra clue to its c. 1930's origin. $1,300.00 fair to
good condition. Private Collection.

**PLATE 82**
A 4¾" (12 cm) Teddyli from the 1950's is shown
here dressed in felt overalls and a checked shirt
with rubber-like latex hands and feet (some crack-
ing) and a Teddy Baby style head. Dressed bears are
always popular among collectors and this marvelous miniature is no exception. $850.00. Private
Collection.

**PLATE 83**
Hi there! Who wouldn't want to wave back to this
friendly little 6" (15 cm) panda from Steiff? This bear
from the mid to late 1950's has an open felt mouth,
black and brown glass eyes, gray synthetic suede paw
pads (earliest versions had felt pads), and a raised
script button. $450.00 up. Courtesy Carol Porter.

**PLATE 84**
The 5" (12.5 cm) panda on all fours was introduced in 1955.
This fine example has the original chest tag with bell and the
ear-tag with a raised script button. $300.00. Courtesy Carol
Porter.

**PLATE 86**
The 1980's 3½" (9 cm) "bendy" bear on the left of caramel mohair wears a Scarlett O'Hara costume by Susan Wheeler. The green bows in her "hair" give just the right touch to this southern bear belle. Her dashing bear beau on the right (early 1980's) wears a custom-knit hat and sweater, more suitable for the ski slopes than a ball or barbecue. $75.00 each. Private Collection.

**PLATE 85**
It may not be a true Teddy, but Steiff made their cuddly koala bear in several sizes from the mid 1950's to the early 1960's. This 5" (12 cm) model has the ear-tag intact with a raised script button, bendable arms and legs with detailed felt hands and feet. $450.00. Courtesy Carol Porter.

**PLATE 87**
Four Teddy-head pins, #8495/03 through 8498/03, came in white, caramel, gold, and brown mohair and were sold in individual plastic containers in the early 1980's. An incised Script button in the left ear and a red bow at the throat make them cute and collectible examples of bear-wear. A blurb from the "Great Steiff Bear Catalog" (mid-1980's) describes their intended use: "Mohair Teddy Pins, constant companions wherever you go. Pin the bear onto your coat, shirt or jacket and he will be with you everywhere. A bright red ribbon makes him ready for the most formal black tie affair or a friend's birthday party." $25.00 each.

**PLATE 88**
This 4" (10 cm) chocolate brown, fully jointed bear is an early 1980's version of the Original Teddybear, purchased with the white ruff around his neck. The yellow cloth-weave ear-tag places him between 1982 and 1987. Available in a variety of colors, his height is the same as earlier Original bears, but the plastic eyes, large head and body, and ears sewn directly into the head seams give this bear a more contemporary look. $60.00.

**PLATE 89**
A 1.25" (3 cm) cast metal bear brooch (#8500/03) was available in 1983 to commemorate the 80th anniversary of Steiff Teddy Bears. This high quality, gold-plated, costume pin had a tiny ear tag incised with the word Steiff, but the arms and legs were stationary. A card inside the box reads: "My name is Teddy. I am your little golden replica of the Original Steiff bear, now celebrating its 80th birthday. I hope I may be your good luck charm."

**PLATE 90**
How to dress in high Steiff style! This fully jointed bear from the 1980's is actually a gold-plated pendant, ¾" (2 cm), that comes in a plastic box with its picture embossed in gold. $25.00.

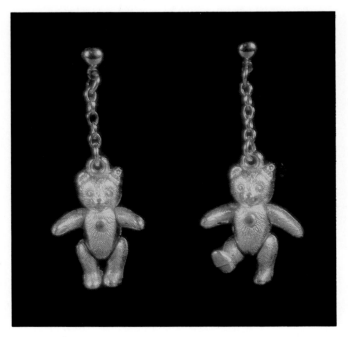

**PLATE 91**
No woman's wardrobe can be complete without these ½" (1.5 cm) baby bear earrings. This smallest pair of Steiff Teddies has jointed arms and legs that dance daintily as the wearer shakes her head. $30.00.

Chapter Four

# Miniature Schuco Bears

Schuco. To a miniature bear collector there is something magical about that word. Technically, it is a trademark abbreviation for the true company name, Schreyer u. Co, but to a bear lover it stands for sheer delight.

The tiny Teddies manufactured by Schuco from the 1920's through the 1970's are unique and original. From the nodding, strutting and tumbling Teds to the frivolously feminine bears whose bellies coquettishly concealed a compact or perfume, these treasured mohair marvels in jewel-like colors have earned their creator, Heinrich Müller, a place in history as the "Fabeargé" of miniature bear-makers.

Herr Müller, an ingenious inventor born in 1886, parlayed an inherent, whimsical creativity and an acquired mechanical know-how into his own German toy company, which eventually achieved world-wide admiration and respect. Müller founded his business in Nuremberg in 1912, with Heinrich Schreyer as a financial partner (hence the name Schreyer u. Co.).

Müller's imaginative enthusiasm and personal dedication to the company survived several partnership changes and two World Wars until his death in 1958. Müller's company continued without him until production ended around the mid 1970's, but thanks to his life's work and the clever designs he left behind, collectors of today still cherish their small Schucos, which are some of the best and most beloved little bears ever made.

Müller's most significant contribution to miniatures was the invention of a new manufacturing process, which allowed Schuco to produce small mohair bears from 5" (13 cm) to 2⅜" (6 cm) with almost no sewing involved. An American patent was filed on April 2, 1923, to protect his idea for a "Toy figure covered with fabric."

Müller's intent was clear from what he stated in the text:

*"It is a well-known fact that it is impossible or very difficult to produce stuffed toy figures of fabric in small sizes in good imitations true to nature. The reason, therefore, is that the fineness of the lines and of the expression are very much obliterated owing to the comparatively coarse stuffing material used, this inconvenience increasing the smaller the figures are. The sewing work becomes more difficult the smaller the size of the figures is so that suf-ficiently clever seamstresses are not available in sufficient number.*

*This invention has for its object to produce fabric covered figures without body or members stuffed with a soft material with the aid of hollow parts pressed from sheet metal or similar material. ...A figure according to this invention is covered with fabric in such a manner that it is of absolutely natural appearance. In order to obtain this result, inwardly projecting teeth are arranged in proximity to the edges of the several hollow parts for composing the figure, these teeth being designed to grip into the fabric after the corresponding hollow part in the edge of the same has been covered with the fabric."*

The adjoining patent drawings show just how well-conceived Müller's idea was. (See Plates 92 – 93.) Every metal nook and notch was perfectly planned, right down to the holes in the snout where floss would be used to sew the nose and mouth, so "the sewing thread serves at the same time for uniting the two halves of the head." The metal ears also helped join the head together, and socket holes were designed to accept eyes with studs which could be bent against the inner head wall and "serve at the same time for holding the fabric."

A previous invention of Müller's which had proved successful in larger "stuffed" animals was the "yes/no" mechanism for which an American patent was filed on April 18, 1921. Clearly, he saw the potential to utilize this in the miniature toy figures as well. Figure 1 on the patent drawing for number 1,585,558, shows the telltale rod and tube connecting the bear's head and body. Further, the text plainly states that "This invention has further for its object to construct the figure in such a manner that the mechanisms for producing the rotating and nodding movements of the head can be easily mounted in the figure..."

The 5" (13 cm) "yes/no" bears, which were born from this idea, are highly prized today. The rounded heads with their innocent faces invite handling, and the sturdy metal bodies with their comfortable size and weight allay any fears of fragility. The smooth-working limbs and mohair-covered "turning" tail encourage play, so Teddy can appear to "talk" in the way Müller imagined, "...as if the head moved without outer influence."

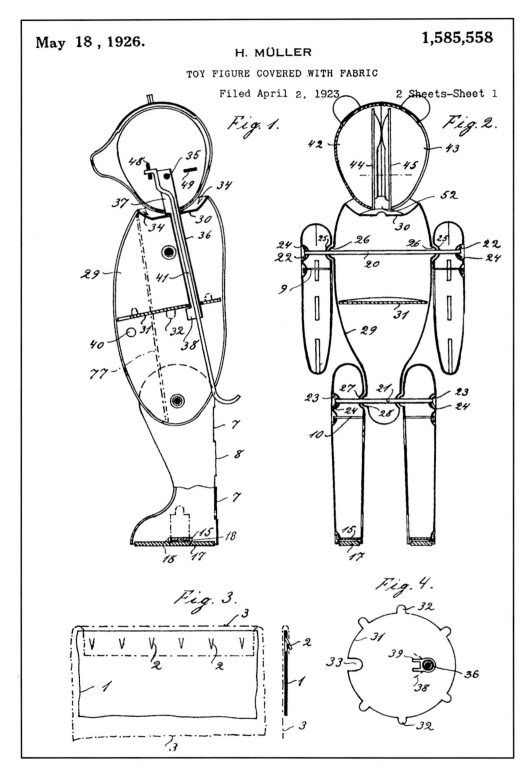

May 18 , 1926.

1,585,558

H. MÜLLER

TOY FIGURE COVERED WITH FABRIC

Filed April 2, 1923      2 Sheets—Sheet 1

Fig. 1.

Fig. 2.

Fig. 3.

Fig. 4.

**PLATE 92**
Müller's concept of the fabric-covered metal bear is seen here from two angles. Figure 3 shows
how the fabric is to be attached to the metal, and Figure 4 is the inner support for the body.

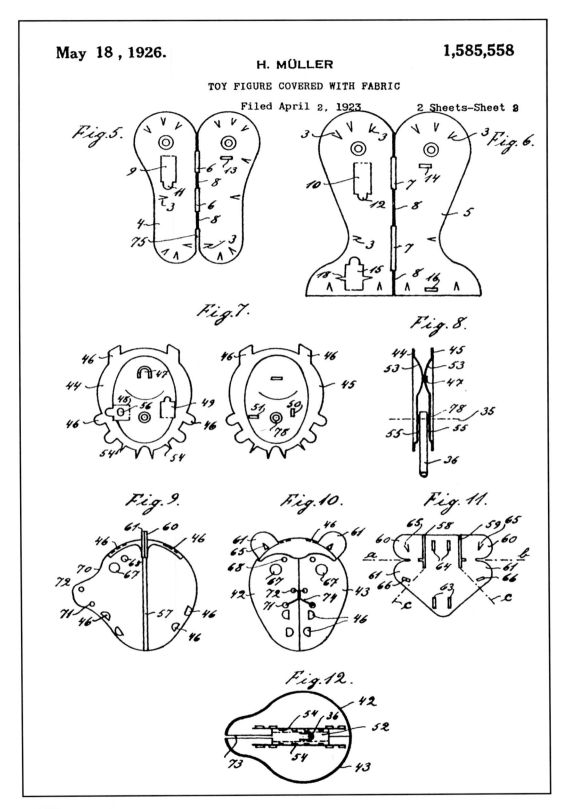

May 18, 1926.

H. MÜLLER

1,585,558

TOY FIGURE COVERED WITH FABRIC

Filed April 2, 1923

2 Sheets—Sheet 2

**PLATE 93**
The internal complexity of Schuco bears is evident from this patent drawing which shows the arms, legs, head, and ears in skeleton form. Note: Schuco yes/no bears were produced from the 1920's through the 1960's, but most of the 5" (13 cm) examples that follow are probably post-WWII.

43

An excerpt from a pre-WWII Schuco trade catalog describes the "Cloth Animals and Figures with Patent Movable Head" as follows: "A gentle, scarcely perceptible movement of the tail is sufficient to turn and nod the animal's head in all directions in a most lifelike manner. These movements are surprisingly true to nature, and grown-ups, especially ladies, are often more fascinated by them than children. Up-to-date as they are, and because of their originality, these cloth animals and figures with the patent movable heads have become most popular, modern gifts." (See Plates 94 – 101.)

**PLATE 95**
Fancy-colors were a Schuco forte. This 5" (13 cm) light tan/apricot-toned Teddy, is a yes/no with its original ribbon intact, and a good example of how different dye-lots can produce subtle changes in shading. $500.00 up.

**PLATE 94**
The upward-curved tail of this 5" (13 cm) tan mohair Teddy immediately gives it away as a yes/no bear. It's surprising to learn that such a smooth and elegant-looking bear has such an intricate design underneath. Müller's true genius lay in making elaborate ideas appear simple. $400.00 up. Private Collection.

**PLATE 96**
A white bear in mint condition like this 5" (13 cm) yes/no is rare and desirable. The horizontally stitched floss nose (light brown) and original ribbon (blue) are typical Schuco traits. $500.00 up. Private Collection.

**PLATE 97**
This 5" (13 cm), yes/no Schuco is covered in a delicious, dark chocolate brown mohair. The characteristic brown eyes with black pupils give him a wide-eyed expression. $450.00 up. Private Collection.

**PLATE 98**
Yes/no Schuco Teddies from the 1950's frequently come with red felt tongues. The 5" (13 cm) bear is rarely found in black. Shades of tan and gold are the most common. $600.00 up. Private Collection.

**PLATE 99**
The Schuco Panda is a perpetual favorite in this smallest 5" (13 cm) yes/no size with brown and black glass eyes, black airbrushed eye rims and chest area. The outstanding condition and an original red ribbon add to this bear's appeal. $600.00 up. Private Collection.

**PLATE 100**
The traditional symbol for the city of West Berlin is a bear, and this 5" (13 cm) brown Schuco "Berlin Bear" proclaims his loyalty with a bold ribbon banner and a gold metal crown. $700.00 up. Private Collection.

**PLATE 101**
This 5" (13 cm) "Berlin Bear" is missing his crown, but the white mohair makes him an unusual example of a yes/no bear. $700.00 up. Private Collection.

Müller's next innovation, which holds particular interest for miniature enthusiasts, was described in an American patent filed in the United States on April 8, 1925, and in Germany on August 22, 1921. It is likely that the previous patent, number 1,585,558, was also filed in Germany before U.S. application was made, but from descriptions found in the text it is logical to conclude that this next idea for a "Fabric-Covered Toy Figure" came shortly afterwards. (See Plates 102 – 103.)

Patent 1,608,904, documents Müller's concept: "This invention relates to toy figures made of sheet metal and covered with fabric, and it relates especially to the manner in which the fabric is fixed on the body of the figure and on the members of the same and to the arrangement which makes it possible to form the several members and to put the same together after the several elements have been covered with fabric. ...Figure 1 shows the toy figure in vertical section. The fabric cover is indicated by dash and dot lines, in the hollow body of the figure a bottle shaped insertion is shown."

Here then, is the inventor's plan for the fabulous 3½" (9 cm) and 5" (13 cm) perfume and bottle bears that followed. Figure 8 and wire rod 20 show alternate methods for jointing the bear when a bottle was used. The head of the bear was designed with "an elastic metal sleeve" inside to facilitate its removal and to keep the bottle insertion snugly closed when the head was in place. These Teddies were available as a "scent-bottle with ground glass stopper," or as a "re-fill flask bottle with cork stopper." (See Plates 104 – 115.)

This patent, #1,608,904, with the body parts more simplified than those of #1,585,558, and with a new method for jointing a head without the yes/no mechanism (Figure 16), was probably the one that facilitated making the truly tiny miniatures, only 2⅜" (6 cm) in height.

Note Figure 5, where #17, "a piece of cloth which forms the hands of a figure" is inserted into the arm. The previous patent also mentions that "The arms of the figure remain open at the lower ends so that pieces of other fabric than that used for covering the toy figure may be inserted to form the hands or paws." The smaller bears, 3½" (9 cm) or under, seem to have been first made with felt paws in place, in the same manner as Schuco monkeys.

The patent evidence shows that Müller developed the bear and monkey designs contiguously, and it is probable that the arms, legs, and bodies of the early Teddies were made on monkey molds. A comparison of these two figures shows that if we take into account the greater depth of the bear's mohair compared to the monkey's felt, the body and limb sizes appear identical. (See Plate 116.)

One collector, now in her early seventies, recalls visiting a small toy store located on the downtown "circle" of Indianapolis around 1931. As a nine-year old girl, she had never loved dolls, but a young man in the store showed her a small, 2⅜" (6 cm), Schuco Teddy with the felt paws attached, which she recalls as a "perfect little bear." The man explained that Teddy had thin metal strips embedded in his feet which could be bent slightly to allow him to stand. The girl purchased the deep golden-colored bear for the significant sum of fifty cents and named him "Speck."

On subsequent trips to Indianapolis over the next two to three years, the girl acquired matching friends for "Speck" in white and dark brown. The three bear buddies shared a dresser drawer which the girl converted into a bear-house, complete with a colored-on door and windows, a garden, and a living room furnished with flocked Tootsie-toy metal furniture. Anytime the girl was sick in bed, the bear-house drawer with its friendly residents was beside her.

When the girl grew into a young woman of high-school age, she happened onto another little Schuco with felt hands and feet, this time in solid black. She "couldn't resist" adopting him, even though by this time, around 1938 – 39, the price had escalated to a dollar or two.

The woman managed to save her four furry friends through the years, even though a couple were innocently injured by an over-playful cat. The bears were lovingly repaired and are still with their original owner today.

Besides giving us a nostalgic look back into childhood pleasures, this woman's story indicates that the tiniest felt-paw Schucos were available at least until 1940. It is probable that production of these bears, many of which have "Germany" stamped on one foot in ink, ended around World War II. (See Plates 117 – 118.)

Because of the success of these smallest bears, it is likely that the company went on to make different dies meant particularly for more Teddy-like (non-monkey) arms and legs. This resulted in the 2¾" (7 cm) model (#7300/7) with straight arms and upward curled feet sans felt and a slightly larger head. Eliminating the felt pads in bears would lower the cost of labor and materials and was obviously an economic advantage. The bear designs certainly did not suffer from this development, rather the figures took on a more traditional Teddy appearance.

Exactly when the change took place is difficult to document, but I have seen examples of the 2¾" (7 cm) bears, which, based on the quality and color of the mohair, appear to be very early. The wilder, more vivid fancy colors seem to indicate an earlier age for these Teddies. Some time overlap in production of the two sizes (6 and 7 cm) must have occurred. A 3½" (9 cm) version, (model #7300/9) was also made, probably shortly after the inception of #7300/7. (See Plates 119 – 132.)

46

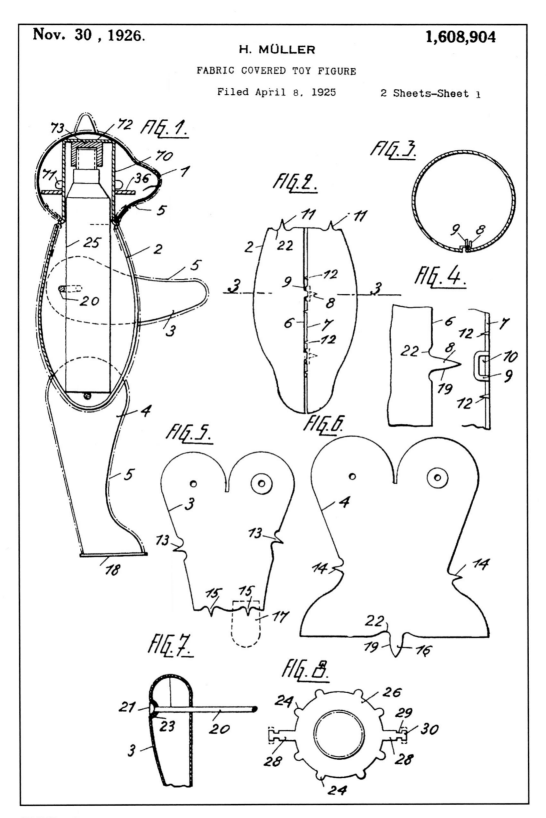

Nov. 30 , 1926.

H. MÜLLER

1,608,904

FABRIC COVERED TOY FIGURE

Filed April 8, 1925    2 Sheets—Sheet 1

**PLATE 102**
This patent drawing from 1925 shows Heinrich Müller's original concept of the "Perfume Bear." The bottle meant to be inserted into the bear's hollow body is visible in Figure 1. The arms and legs are more simplified in design than the earlier patent, and a paw insertion (#17) is shown in Figure 5.

### H. MÜLLER

FABRIC COVERED TOY FIGURE

Filed April 8, 1925          2 Sheets—Sheet 2

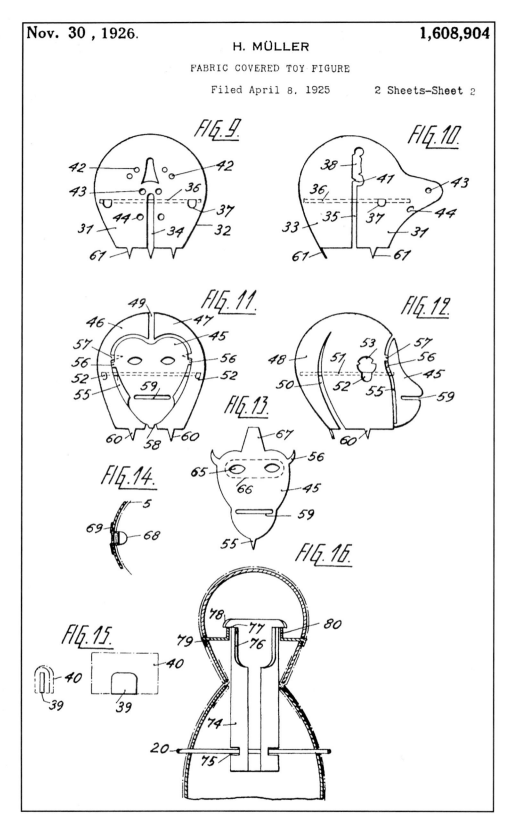

**PLATE 103**

This drawing shows the method for jointing the head of a non-perfume bear (Figure 16), a method for covering the cardboard ear with fabric (Figure 15), and a method of attaching metal eyes to their sockets (Figure 14). It shows front and side views of the bear and monkey heads (Figures 9-13). Note: the following "bottle" bears are all c. 1925 – 1955.

PLATE 104 (left)
This 5" (13 cm) Schuco bottle bear is a fine example of a very desirable Teddy. Deep gold is the most common color, but this bear's mint condition and charismatic face with black painted metal eyes and horizontally-stitched black floss nose make him a welcome addition to any collection. $600.00 up.

PLATE 105 (above)
The bear's head is removed by means of an inner "elastic sleeve" and the hidden glass bottle is revealed. A cork stopper was supplied on some bottle bears intended for use as re-fillable flasks.

PLATE 106 (left)
This 5" (13 cm) lavender bottle bear is nearly identical to the previous Teddy except for its wild and wonderful color. Lavender-water would be the perfect scent to store inside! $900.00 up. Private Collection.

PLATE 107 (above)
The head is removed here to reveal the bottle inside with cork stopper.

**PLATE 108**
This 5" (13 cm) fuschia-toned bottle bear has some minor mohair loss and wear, but the color is interesting and unusual. $800.00 up. Private Collection.

**PLATE 109**
Metal Schuco spectacles give this 5" (13 cm) basic gold bottle bear a studious sort of smile and turn a common colored Teddy into an uncommon collectible. $700.00 up. Private Collection.

**PLATE 110**
This wonderful white perfume bear has the black painted metal eyes typical of Schuco, with a nose stitched in light brown floss. Most amazing is this bear's fine condition. White bears are usually the first to show signs of handling and wear. $800.00 up. Courtesy Harriet Purtill.

**PLATE 111**
This sweet little lavender perfume Teddy is only 3½" (9 cm) tall. With her attached felt paws, she is surely one of Schuco's earliest examples. $1,000.00 up. Private Collection.

PLATE 112 (left)
In bright gold, this 3½" Teddy with black metal eyes and black floss nose appears to be a basic Schuco bear. But don't pass him by without trying a tiny tug on the head....

PLATE 113 (above)
Teddy's secret surprise is revealed in the form of a perfect perfume bottle inside his mint condition body. Of the two perfume sizes, this is more rare and more coveted by collectors. $800.00 up. Private Collection.

PLATE 114 (left)
The fancy apricot color, desirable size, and condition give this 3½" (9 cm) perfume bear more features to love. $1,000.00 up.

PLATE 115 (above)
With her head removed, the tiny bottle can be seen.

**PLATE 116**
Schuco's tiniest monkeys and bears show an amazing similarity in size and style. The bear's head is larger, but it's obvious that the bear and monkey arms and legs were stamped from the same metal molds. Monkey, $125.00; bear, $275.00 up.

**PLATE 117**
Two little Schucos standing side by side are the same 2⅜" (6 cm) size as "Speck" and his buddies. Black and white are both more difficult to find than the basic bear colors. This style also came in pink, and who knows what other super Schuco colors you might find? $300.00 up. Courtesy Harriet Purtill.

52

**PLATE 118**
These 2⅜" (6 cm) brown and gold Teddies are classic examples of Schuco's earliest miniature bear style. Any minis this size with the felt paws in place were made from the early 1920's probably through the late 1930's. $275.00 up. Courtesy Harriet Purtill.

**PLATE 119**
With the mohair covering removed, this 2¾" (7 cm) Schuco skeleton reveals the sturdy metal body with its smart, sophisticated design.

**PLATE 120**
Not only is this 2¾" (7 cm) vermillion Teddy an odd color, but his ears look way too big! They appear to be metal underneath the mohair and might be an experimental size? Either that, or somebody goofed and gave this poor little Teddy, c. 1930, the ears intended for a bigger bear. $250.00 up. Courtesy Harriet Purtill.

**PLATE 121**
A bright gold 2¾" (7 cm) Teddy and a caramel colored friend share the Schuco spotlight. Even though these colors are fairly common, and their age is rather recent, c. 1970, every Schuco miniature is considered collectible. Besides, how could anyone resist? $150.00 up.

**PLATE 122**
Here the 3½" (9 cm) and 2¾" (7 cm) Teddies are shown together for size comparison. Both have the trademark metal eyes and floss noses. The larger bear still wears his original red ribbon. $165.00 up each.

**PLATE 123**
According to Elizabeth Bentley Hamilton in her winter 1984 article from *Teddy Bear and Friends* magazine, this 2¾" (7 cm), c. 1974 Schuco "was chosen as an 'ambassador' by the New York City office of the Public Relations Department of the City of West Berlin, which has as its symbol the bear. Adorned with a metal crown, 'Berliner Bear' wore a sash of white between two red borders, stamped in back with the words: 'Berlin ist eine Reisewert' (Berlin is a travel value). Intended for wearing, a small pin was placed to the back of teddy's head." $185.00 up.

**PLATE 124**
This 2¾" (7 cm) Schuco Teddy, c. 1960 – 1970, sports an unusual-colored mohair coat in a lovely shade somewhere between cinnamon and apricot. Dye lots may vary from bolt to bolt of mohair, so color differences can occur even among the gold and brown tones. $185.00 up.

**PLATE 125**
Dressed in their Sunday best, this c. 1950's Schuco set of family bears 3½" (9 cm) and 2¾" (7 cm) was outfitted by F.A.O. Schwartz toy store. Dad wears a black felt suit with tiny black buttons and a cream satin bow tie, while Mother's dress is made of semi-sheer yellow organdy with polka-dot trim. White panties, a lace-trimmed petticoat, and a cream lace scarf complete her ensemble. A gold buttoned, yellow felt vest and light brown felt pants accent the boy bear's fur of tan mohair. The clothes are non-removable, and give these basic-colored bears extra style and desirability. $550.00 for the set. Courtesy Harriet Purtill.

**PLATE 126**
This bear pair from Schuco shows the two smallest sizes of Pandas they made, in 3½" (9 cm) and 2¾" (7 cm). White mohair-covered bodies with black ears, arms and legs make these two Teddies cute and collectible. Small, $175.00; large, $200.00. Private Collection.

**PLATE 127**
This 2¾" (7 cm) beige bear has factory-original clothes. His gold felt overalls are held up by cord straps that cross in the back and a felt "handkerchief" decorates the front pocket. A felt-covered metal cap had "shell" written across it on some examples. Presumably these bears were made as promotional mascots for Shell gas stations in Germany and came with cords to hang from the rearview mirror. $650.00 up. Private Collection.

**PLATE 128**
A paper label remains intact in the arm of this 3½" (9 cm) light brown bear. "Made in Western Germany" is printed on one side, with "64% wool, 36% cotton" on the other. These paper or linen-like labels were inserted in the arms or legs of Schucos intended for export. $165.00 up each.

**PLATE 129**
These three Teddies (3½"/9 cm) in classic shades of gold, tan and caramel mohair all retain their original red ribbon bows. $165.00 up. Courtesy Michelle Daunton.

PLATE 130
A white Schuco in mint condition like this beautiful 3½" (9 cm) bear is a rare find, guaranteed to tempt the most discriminating Teddy collector. $350.00 up. Courtesy Donna Harrison West.

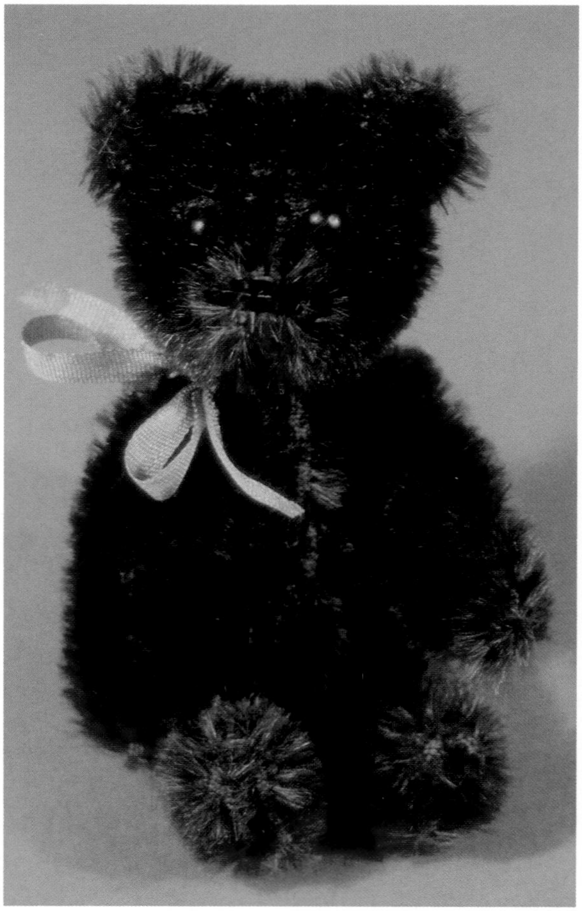

PLATE 131
A sure cure for the bear blues is this 3½" (9 cm) Schuco Ted in bright blue mohair. Not only is Teddy in mint condition, (ribbon not original) but his color is exceptional and rare. $700.00 up. Private Collection.

PLATE 132
An original green ribbon accentuates the unusual peach-colored mohair and red floss nose on this 3½" (9 cm) Schuco. $225.00 up.

A 1937 catalog account of the small, basic bears reads: "These Miniature Figures may count beauty of form and shape and also a neat clean finish amongst their special qualities, for which they are indebted to the patent mechanical process of manufacture. Because of the great variety in which these articles are produced and finished, these little animals are both toys and objects of fun and jokes. The above are supplied as far as possible in various colors, i.e. gold, red, pink, lilac, green, brown, etc."

Although most Schuco miniatures were not marked with the company name or trademark, they are not difficult for a knowledgeable collector to identify. Many of the novelty items are so unique that no one else could have made them. Even the basic jointed bears are characterized by heft, style and appearance. Fabric coverings were always mohair, felt, or velvet; eyes were made of painted metal in the 2⅜" (6 cm) up to 5" (13 cm) sizes, glass or fancy-colored cut glass in the 5" (13 cm) or larger sizes.

Some Schuco-like reproductions are available, but most can be distinguished from the originals by synthetic fabrics and plastic eyes and/or noses. Refer to Chapter Eight for photos and further information on these.

At the end of World War II, (from approximately 1948 – 1953), a linen label reading on one side "Made in U.S. Zone Germany" and on the other side "64% wool, 36% cotton" was inserted into the animal's leg or arm seam. This label later read "Made in Western Germany" and eventually changed to paper. A distinctive style of dull,

woven ribbon was used in various colors to decorate the neck on some models. A silk bow was placed on 9 cm and larger bears from the 1930's, but ribbons were apparently not available on the smallest (6 and 7 cm) sizes.

Lateral gaps in the head (figure 10 of Plate 103) were designed to hold the ears and "As shown in Figure 15, the ear consists of a piece of cardboard covered with cloth." The previous patent used metal for the ears, and it is sometimes difficult to detect what hard substance lies beneath the mohair covering.

On most Schucos, even the smallest, ears appear to be metal, although pipe cleaners were used on some later models. Many of the 3½" (9 cm) and 5" (13 cm) bears have sewn mohair ears with nothing underneath (compacts and bottle bears in these sizes usually had hard ears). Most in the 2¾" (7 cm) size had hard, covered ears up until late in production. Trying to date your bears by differences in ear construction may not be conclusive.

The 7 and 9 cm bears and pandas were packed by the dozen in orange-red cardboard boxes. The top of the box folded upward to make an enticing bear-head display for the retail store. This feature was referred to in the catalog as a "silent salesman," and the bears were said to be available in assorted colors. "Original Schuco Talisman" was written across the top, and four cavorting bears were drawn in various positions across the bottom, presumably to demonstrate the playful possibilities of their jointed heads and limbs. (See Plates 133 – 134.)

**PLATE 133**
Four 2¾" (7 cm) Schucos, c. 1950's, remain mint in their original box, 7½" long by 2½" high by 2½" deep. This fabulous collector's fantasy allows us to imagine what it was like to buy the bears from our local store. The sides read "Made in Western Germany" and Importe d'Allemagne. The original stock number, 7300/7 is shown on the back. $800.00 up for the set.

**PLATE 134**
A profusion of Pandas, six in all, are still mint in their original box, 8½" long by 2¾" high by 3¾" deep. The Panda stock number for these 3½" (9 cm) bears, 7303/9, is shown on the back of the box. Their red cotton ribbons are all intact, along with linen-like arm labels that read "Made in U.S. Zone Germany," dating them somewhere between 1948 and 1953. How would you like to find these guys for sale at your neighborhood toy shop for the outrageous sum of 98 cents apiece? A rare grouping like this might be compared to a matched set of pearls, where the group value exceeds the sum of the individual items. Replacing the set would be nearly impossible. $1,600.00 up for the set.

Müller's next invention relating to miniatures was an "Eye for Plush Toy Figures," for which an American patent was filed on January 20, 1925. Müller's object was "...to give the eyes a more animated expression which is more true to life than the eyes possess which are presently used and which mostly consist of one single glass body. ...it has already become known to use as eyes glass bodies which are cut after the manner of a brilliant or diamond in order to obtain a more vivid brightness..." (See Plate 135.)

Müller goes on to explain that brilliant cut eyes had previously been glued into toy figures of wood or celluloid, but his idea was to mount the eye in a metal bezel that could be used in plush animals. The advantage, he said, was "that not the whole eye must consist of glass, but merely the central part of the same which corresponds with the pupil so that the eye has a quite natural appearance."

This invention was advertised by Schuco as "Sparkling Eyes" and apparently could only be obtained by special order, probably due to the added expense. Because of the relative rarity, they do add some interest and value, but are only found on 5" (13 cm) or larger bears, and seem to be most popular on perfumes. (See Plates 136 – 142.)

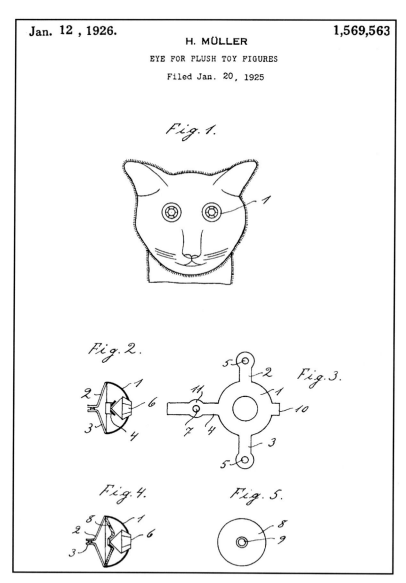

Jan. 12 , 1926.  
H. MÜLLER  
1,569,563  
EYE FOR PLUSH TOY FIGURES  
Filed Jan. 20, 1925  

Fig. 1.  
Fig. 2.  
Fig. 3.  
Fig. 4.  
Fig. 5.  

**PLATE 135**
**The above drawing is for Heinrich Müller's patent #1,569,563 entitled "Eye for Plush Toy Figures." Although the animal pictured is a cat, the "Sparkling Eyes" feature illustrated, with a brilliant-cut stone set in an attachable metal bezel, was also available in Schuco bears 5" (13 cm) or larger. Early perfume bottle bears seem to be the most frequent recipients of these special-order eyes.**

**PLATE 136**
A 5" (13 cm) red perfume bottle bear is more rare with his patented, cut-crystal eyes. $1,000.00 up. Private Collection.

**PLATE 137**
This deep gold color is the most common shade seen in 5" (13 cm) Schuco perfumes, but this particular perfume Teddy has "Sparkling Eyes" an extra, fancy feature that sets him apart from the crowd. $700.00 up. Private Collection.

**PLATE 138**
The long, white mohair on this 5" (13 cm) Schuco perfume shows just how much difference a change in fabric can make. The bear is made in the same size and pattern as other Schuco perfumes, but the finished Teddy is fuller, with a softer, less classic style. "Sparkling Eyes" and a brown floss nose add to the unusual effect. $1,000.00 up. Private Collection.

**PLATE 139**
A vibrant coat of vivid orange mohair and flashing, jeweled eyes give this rare 5" (13 cm) Schuco perfume a delightfully different look. $1,000.00 up. Private Collection.

**PLATE 140**
Light gold, super-silky mohair combined with faceted, golden-jewel eyes and a perfume bottle hidden inside its body, raise this 5" (13 cm) Schuco Teddy to the height of little-bear luxury. $1,000.00 up. Private Collection.

**PLATE 141**
This pink Schuco bottle bear is designed in the 3½" (9 cm) size, but a special pin attached to the back allows him to become more closely attached to you. See Plate 142. $1,000.00 up.

**PLATE 142**
The pin-back is easily visible from this rear view with the words "Schuco Patent, Made in Germany" inscribed on the metal base of the rare bear. An original stock tag also remains with the numbers 811/2/9 identifying the model. Private Collection.

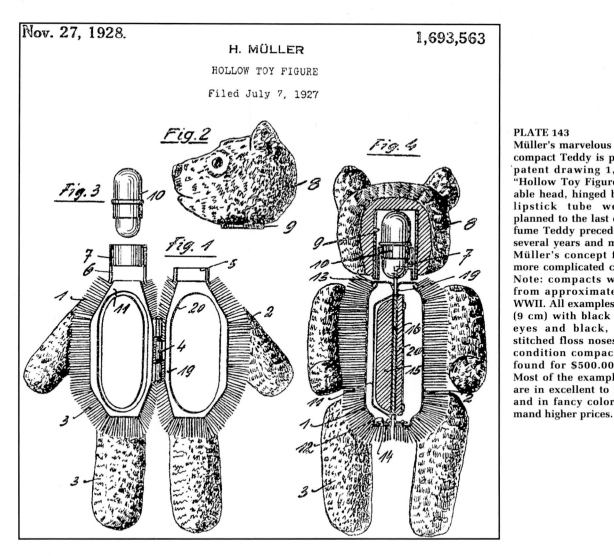

H. MÜLLER

1,693,563

HOLLOW TOY FIGURE

Filed July 7, 1927

*Fig.2*

*Fig.3*

*Fig.4*

*Fig.1*

**PLATE 143**
Müller's marvelous invention for a compact Teddy is pictured here in patent drawing 1,693,563 for a "Hollow Toy Figure." The removable head, hinged body, and little lipstick tube were carefully planned to the last detail. The perfume Teddy preceded this idea by several years and may have led to Müller's concept for the clever, more complicated compact design. Note: compacts were available from approximately 1927 until WWII. All examples shown are 3½" (9 cm) with black painted metal eyes and black, horizontally-stitched floss noses. Fair to good condition compacts can still be found for $500.00 to $1,000.00. Most of the examples shown here are in excellent to mint condition and in fancy colors, which command higher prices.

Another of Müller's amazing ideas was to incorporate a woman's powder compact inside a 3½" (9 cm) bear. The patent application for this miniature treasure, filed July 7, 1927, gives a detailed, if somewhat dry, description of the fanciful toy. Müller referred to the item as "a vanity case in the form of a hollow toy figure adapted to be opened, and has for its object to provide an article of this character which will be unique in appearance and which will hold various toilet articles in such a manner as to be conveniently reached and used."

Müller further suggests for the hollow area in the neck that "a capsule containing a lipstick or any other useful article may be stored." How practical! (See Plate 143.)

The end result was the wonderfully feminine Teddy named "Miss Vanity" or "Miss Whoopee Vanity" (probably during the roaring twenties). This ladylike bear came in quite a few fancy colors, enough choices to please any girl or girl at heart. (See Plates 144 – 153.)

Several interesting modifications of the "compact" yielded new bears with different surprises inside. A "Glücksbar" or Lucky Bear opened to reveal a stomach lined with shiny pink fabric, containing small plastic charms in the form of lucky elephants, babies, pigs, or dice, or some combination thereof. Another option was the Manicure Bear which the 1937, 25th anniversary Schuco catalog described as "fitted with Nail-file and Cleaner, Cuticle Remover, Nail Polishing Stick, and Polisher."

The same catalog page announces that "As Scent Bottles or Flasks, Powder and Manicure Boxes of original shape and design, these Miniature Figures have established a place of their own amongst Gift Articles. They are delightfully charming and enjoy a widespread demand" — timeless words that are twice as true today. (See Plates 154 – 157.)

Heinrich Müller's mechanical ingenuity gave birth to several miniature "motion" Teddies. The somersaulting bear was a highly successful toy for Schuco, and Müller patented a tumbling mechanism with a new fly wheel configuration as early as 1920, but this was apparently only used on larger bears. Unlike the bigger tumbling Teddies, the miniature versions were key wound and spring driven.

**PLATE 144**
This lovely 3½" (9 cm) lavender compact came in an original blue cardboard box with the Schuco trademark at the top left corner and "Miss Whoopee Vanity" written across the front. Teddy's whimsical name certainly has a "Twenties" ring to it, but is pertinent for the 1990's as well—finding a treasure like this would make any Schuco-lover scream whoopee! $1,200.00 up. Courtesy D.A. Horton.

**PLATE 145**
"Miss Whoopee Vanity" is seen here with her head removed and the printing "Made in Germany" visible on the back of the very rare box. Later compact boxes read simply "Miss Vanity."

**PLATE 146**
Pink mohair adds to the inherent appeal of this fanciful,
and decidedly feminine little compact bear (3½"/9 cm).
$1,000.00 up. Private Collection.

**PLATE 147**
Teddy's head is removed to reveal the secret inside with the lipstick tube at top still intact.

**PLATE 148**
Who knows how many lucky young ladies of the 1920's
or 1930's received a bright green Schuco compact bear
like this for Christmas? I suspect that quite a few compact fans were way past the age of childhood associated
with Teddy Bears. The powder and lipstick inside would
surely appeal to women as well, and give them a perfect
"excuse" to buy an otherwise "forbidden" bear. $1,000.00
up. Private Collection.

**PLATE 149**
A hard, pink tablet of sweet-smelling powder lures the owner to open her bear.

**PLATE 150**
Red is one of the favorite and most sought-after colors of many compact fans. This 3½" (9 cm) Teddy is still beautifully bright and unfaded after 60 + years. $1,100.00 up.

**PLATE 151**
With Teddy's head taken off, the lipstick tube and powder puff are more easily inspected.

**PLATE 152**
This 3½" (9 cm) tangerine mohair Teddy is another fine, fancy-colored compact. $1,000.00 up. Private Collection.

**PLATE 153**
Apricot is a lovely shade for this 3½" (9 cm) compact and shows just how many variations are possible in the Schuco range of deliciously-dyed mohair. $1,000.00 up. Courtesy Harriet Purtill.

**PLATE 154**
This 3½" (9 cm) gold mohair bear appears to be the standard Schuco style, but remember that the word Schuco is often synonymous with surprise.

**PLATE 155**
Teddy's pink satin-lined belly holds three plastic dice and a cream plastic elephant charm. The lucky owner of this rare bear definitely made a fortunate find. $1,100.00 up. Private Collection.

**PLATE 156**
This lavender 3½" (9 cm) mohair Teddy with its original tag intact may be the rarest form in which the "compact" bear design was available.

**PLATE 157**
Inside, a complete manicure set is stored, along with the more standard lipstick tube in Teddy's neck. This exceedingly rare bear has provenance as well: it was given as a bridesmaid's gift in a "rainbow" wedding, where each attendant wore a dress of a different pastel hue. The bride picked small Schuco's in fancy colors to coordinate with her maid's gowns and presented them as keepsakes. How perfectly romantic! Where are all those bridesmaids now?! $1,500.00 up. Photographs courtesy Kathy George.

According to the 1937 catalog, the somersaulting bear came in several miniature sizes, 10 cm, #879, "with artificial silk bow, plush head, and multi-colored felt suit," 12 cm, #873, "with artificial silk bow, plush in gold or other colors" and 13.5 cm, #876 "completely in plush." Narrow, pointed snouts (muzzles were shaved on long-furred models) characterized the earliest models, although shorter-nosed tumblers were also available in the late 1930's. (See Plates 158 – 164.)

**PLATE 159**
Like many other Schuco toys, several color combinations were available for each bear. This 3¾" (10 cm) tumbler wears a green felt jacket with pink felt pants in the style of Schuco's other "Bellhop" or messenger bears. $500.00 up. Courtesy Dottie Ayers.

**PLATE 158**
The 3¾" (10 cm) somersaulting or "tumbling" Teddy with his felt jacket and pants, black metal hands and feet and mohair-covered head is an early Schuco clockwork toy from the 1920's. When this frolicsome bear is wound by means of a Schuco-marked key, he tumbles energetically across a table or floor. The long arms are joined by a common axle and propel the bear forward by means of a spring-driven motor. $500.00 up. Private Collection.

**PLATE 160**
A purple felt jacket and orange pants characterize this Teddy tumbler's durable, but colorful clothes (ribbon not original). The left sleeve on most Schuco somersaulting bears shows a small tear where the key rubbed against the arm. And speaking of keys — if you buy a bear without one, a properly-fitting replacement can usually be found, but make sure the bear is in good working order first. Original keys were marked Schuco, and as with most antiques, the more original parts present, the better. $500.00 up. Private Collection.

**PLATE 161**
This 3¾" (10 cm) somersaulting bear wears a blue felt
jacket, orange pants and has his original neck-ribbon
remaining. $500.00 up.

**PLATE 162**
The Schuco acrobat bear also came in this 4¾" (12 cm)
size. This light gold Teddy, c. 1950's, has brown and black
glass eyes, a black floss nose, tan felt paw pads and an
original ribbon. $550.00 up. Private Collection.

**PLATE 163**
This bright red (rare) acrobat bear with its painted metal
eyes and felt covered hands is probably an early version of
this toy from the late 1920's or 1930's. $900.00 up. Private
Collection.

**PLATE 164**
This acrobat bear with its long, yellow-orange mohair
coat is another early example of Schuco's key wound
tumbler. $900.00 up. Private Collection.

Another mechanical marvel invented by Müller is the dancing bear with a clockwork mechanism, the novel feature of which "consists in imparting to the toy a proper reciprocating or vibratory motion which imitates most closely the natural motion of an animal or bird."

The patent drawing for this item is in the shape of a bird, which we know today as the popular Schuco Peck-Peck Bird, but it seems that Müller intended the same mechanism to be used in other animals as well. "In addition to this" he says, "according to my invention the toy may be constructed that it will make a walking, dancing, or similar motion."

And so the idea for miniature dancing bears was born. Several variations of the bear design were made, with different felt outfits (#921, 13 cm or #951, 11 cm), or twirling balls held in the Teddies hands (#964, 13 cm). A Schuco trade catalog states that: "Jolly to look at are these pretty, gaily dressed agile little dancers as they swiftly and long turn round in graceful circles." And "Standing erect without any support these beautifully dressed figures begin dancing in circles as soon as the clockwork in the body is started. The effect produced on the onlookers is simply astounding."

Astounding indeed! Especially to collectors today. (See Plates 165 – 168.)

Toy metal cars were a well-known Schuco staple item, and Müller managed to combine two or more ideas and give some little bears mobility by attaching them to Schuco wheeled vehicles. These "Fly-Wheel Rolling Toys," introduced in the late 1920's, were available as a three-wheeled go-cart with a detachable 3½" (9 cm) bear (#881), or with a non-detachable half-figure (#891), or a 5" (13 cm) felt-suited bear on a scooter (#861). (See Plates 169 – 172.)

**PLATE 165**
This 5" (13 cm) c. 1930's bear is also a Schuco key-wound mechanical. The gold, partially-jointed, mohair Teddy with red felt cap and pants "dances" comically in a circle with its black tassel swinging behind. $900.00 up. Private Collection.

**PLATE 166**
A later (c. 1950's – 1960's) variation of the 5" (13 cm) dancing bear is this captivating Ted with his blue felt jacket and red pants carrying a spinning ball. The head fur is now made of a synthetic plush. $800.00 up. Private Collection.

**PLATE 167**
This dancing Schuco Ted, c. 1930's, is 4¼" (11 cm) high. He wears an orange felt jacket, bright yellow felt pants, and has the characteristic painted metal feet. $800.00 up. Private Collection.

**PLATE 168 (above, right)**
A colorful original box shows the fancy moves this 5" (13 cm) mid-1950's to early 1960's, Schuco dancing bear can make. The ball spins as he turns, showing off his blue felt jacket, red pants, and airbrushed face and ears (synthetic plush). $900.00 up with box. Private Collection.

**PLATE 169 (right)**
A 5" (13 cm) fully jointed gold mohair Schuco bear with black felt pants and red felt cap rides his custom orange three-wheeled scooter, also by Schuco (note the trademark on the scooter's side). This set is not assembled, rather bear and scooter were paired at the factory. $1,100.00 up. Private Collection.

**PLATE 170**
A pink, three-wheeled Schuco car has a built-in seat to carry this 3½" (9 cm) gold Schuco bear. This rare set is also a factory original pair. $1,200.00 up. Private Collection.

**PLATE 171**
This cream-colored metal Schuco car is similar to the one in the previous picture, but the tan mohair bear (which, ouch!, is actually only a half of a bear) sits lower in the Schuco trade-marked vehicle. $1,100.00 up. Private Collection.

**PLATE 172**
This pink metal three-wheeler comes with a matching pink mohair Teddy driver. Müller's love of toy figures and cars is cleverly combined in this rare piece which clearly epitomizes his vision. $1,200.00 up. Private Collection.

Another interesting item often attributed to Schuco is the atomizer Teddy, which consists of a round flat body with four rather stubby arms and legs attached in the appropriate spots, a sewn-on head, and a pair of pointed, oversized ears. A large brass screw forms a base on which the bear stands and allows access for filling the hollow body with perfume. When the stomach of the bear is squeezed, the scent sprays from a tiny brass nozzle in the nose. This weird and wonderful little bear is puzzling in its origin, but remains rare and desirable no matter who the maker was. (See Plates 173 – 175.)

Schuco's range of Teddies and toys was so wide and versatile that collectors are still making new and unusual discoveries. The bright orange boxer in Illustration 176 with his hot pink felt gloves and blue ribbon banner is an interesting variation of the 5" (13 cm) bear. Other, less known items available from the catalog were a pin-on bear with a sneaky, hidden squirt-bulb that propelled water from one arm, a bear bicycle mascot that could be clamped to a handle-bar, a bear designed with a suspension cord for hanging over baby's cradle, a bear with a voice produced by pressing the head onto the body, and a Teddy that served as a table card holder or "bearer" of a congratulatory card.

Around the 1930's Schuco came out with a less commonly known bear that looks similar in style to the successful Steiff Teddy Baby. The painted face, wide smiling mouth and large velvet feet of "Baby Bear" (#821 12) are characteristics not found on other Schuco Teddies. Some of these bears were made with a yes/no mechanism as well. (See Plates 177 – 179.)

**PLATE 173**
This 3¼" (8.5 cm) red mohair atomizer bear is a rare and fascinating item often attributed to Schuco. Perfume squirts out a metal nozzle in the bear's nose as the stomach is squeezed. Unusual non Schuco-like characteristics of this Teddy are its blue and black glass eyes, small stumpy arms, and oversized pointed ears. A large brass screw at the bottom allows access to the hollow body so the perfume can be refilled. $1,500.00 up (good condition). Private Collection.

**PLATE 174**
This 3¼" (8.5 cm) orange velvet atomizer shows the flat body shape and pointed, almost cat-like ears quite clearly. The eyes on this version are faceted black glass beads. $1,200.00 up (fair condition). Courtesy D.A. Horton.

**PLATE 175**
This 3¼" (8.5 cm) atomizer looks a bit more Teddy-like in his coat of dark gold mohair. His eyes are faceted black glass beads (like the orange velvet version), but this mint condition Teddy has no stitching on his nose and apparently never did. The brass screw at the bottom is marked "American Patent A.F. (applied for), Germany." Although I conducted a thorough search for Mr. Müller's American patents, I found no information about this design. Regardless, this is a desirable, if slightly goofy looking Teddy, and represents an original and imaginative idea. $1,500.00 up (mint).

**PLATE 176**
This 5½" (14 cm) orange Schuco Teddy with fuchsia felt boxing gloves and blue-green ribbon banner is a highly unusual bear, c. 1930. Strange and wonderful Schucos surface every now and then, and collectors never know what interesting item they may come across. $1,000.00 up. Private Collection.

**PLATE 177**
This 4¾" (12 cm) cream bear is not made in the usual Schuco style, rather it strongly resembles a Steiff Teddy Baby with its large velvet feet and turned down paws. The word "Germany" is stamped on the bottom of the right paw. This rare and beautifully mint bear is c. 1930's. $800.00 up (mint). Private Collection.

**PLATE 178**
The 4¾" (12 cm) look-alike was also made in this medium brown mohair. $700.00 up. Private Collection.

**PLATE 179**
This bear is identical in style to the Teddy in Illustration 177, except his tail contains the patented Schuco yes/no mechanism. $500.00 (fair condition). Private Collection.

The Schuco soccer team turns up to play occasionally in their different colored uniforms. The bodies are made of a bendable, pipe-cleaner-type material and the large, flat-bottomed plastic soccer shoes help them stand upright (or prepare to score a goal). (See Plate 180.)

The "Janus" bear, from the early 1950's, is a variation of the 3½" (9 cm) bear and described in their 50th anniversary catalog (1962) as "an amusing trick-item. Janus has two different faces, just turn small knob and "Janus" will turn its amiable face into a funny grimace." (See Plate 181.)

A ghoulish grimace is more like it! But nearly any small Schuco face can make a miniature bear collector smile.

**PLATE 180**
These 3½" (9 cm) soccer player bears, c. 1970, similar in shape to the Schuco Mascot series of miniature dressed animals, were made with bendable pipe-cleaner type arms and legs, and outfitted with plastic soccer shoes and uniforms from various German teams. $150.00 up each. Private Collection.

**PLATE 181**
The Schuco Janus bear, named after the Roman city god with two faces, has a regular Teddy face on one side of his head and a funny grimacing expression on the other, complete with plastic tongue that seems to be sticking out. A knob under this c. 1950's Teddy's body turns the head around to the desired position, depending on the mood of the owner. The Teddy on the right still retains a "Made in U.S. Zone Germany" linen tag in its right arm. $650.00 – $700.00 up each. Private Collection.

# Chapter Five

# Japanese Miniatures

Teddies made in Japan may not have the current prestige or collector's clout that German bears enjoy, but these charming miniatures have always filled a different niche. Not all loving parents of the past could afford to purchase a prestigious Steiff at their child's whim. Nor did a small, spur of the moment gift always call for a Schuco. In these cases, a Japanese made bear was just the thing — the right size at the right price.

With the quality of German-made Bears hard to beat, Japanese companies focused their attention on lower-priced Teddies made of less expensive materials and with less intensive labor. The workmanship on these minis cannot compare to more meticulously made bears, but the crude styling is somehow cute. Sophisticated collectors may scoff, but these unique little bears deserve recognition.

Searching for Japanese-made Teddies can be a true collecting treat. For those on a limited bear budget, prices are still reasonable. Unlike Steiff and Schuco items, which are getting harder to find except from a specialized bear dealer, tiny Teds marked "Made in Japan" may still turn up anywhere.

Bears of Japanese origin can usually be determined by the following characteristics: The bodies are hard to the touch, constructed of wood or pressed fiber with a thin, rayon-like fuzzy fabric glued on top. The limbs, which are also of fabric-covered wood, are jointed by a wire running through the torso. The head with molded-on ears is usually not jointed but integrated as one piece with the neck and body.

Eyes are often an amber-colored glass with black pupils inserted into the head via a metal stem. The nose is a slightly domed, black glass disc with a glass stem hidden in the snout. Paw pads, if any are present, are of a glued-on, felt-like fabric. A shiny synthetic ribbon was often tied around the neck and a blue paper label, marked "Made in Japan" may be glued to the back. (See Plates 182 – 184.)

**PLATE 182**
**Close-up features that identify these pre-WWII Japanese minis are the molded-on ears and neck, amber glass eyes with black pupils, and a black glass lentil-shaped nose. The original ribbons around their necks and the glued-on plush fabric both appear to be rayon. $50.00 each.**

**PLATE 183**
This 5" (12.5 cm) light brown rayon plush covered Teddy has glass eyes with a black painted on nose and foot claws. The paw-pads are a glued-on felt-like fabric, and the limbs are string-jointed, but this bear's most interesting feature is the squeaker located in his belly. Pressing downward on the head while Teddy is seated, produces an amusing and appropriately un-ferocious noise. $95.00. Courtesy Elaine Fujita-Gamble.

**PLATE 184**
At 3¼" (8 cm) tall these glass-eyed, gold and cinnamon-colored Teddies have the typical look of Japanese-made miniature from the 1930's. The hard, pressed fiber, one-piece ears, heads and bodies and the applied rayon fabric covering are major clues to their Oriental origin. Original rayon ribbons and blue "Made in Japan" labels still pressed to their backs make identification moot for this mint condition bear pair. $50.00 each.

**PLATE 185**
A downward progression of quality is evident when comparing earlier Japanese Teddies with their more recently-made counterparts. The brown 3¼" (8 cm) bear on the left has a glass nose and eyes and a relatively slender body, neck, and limbs. The late 1970's example at right has a plastic nose and eyes, a fatter body with a nearly non-existent neck and a thicker nylon plush fabric covering. It is possibly a stray from a Teddy Bear School play set imported by Shackman. $30.00 – $50.00.

Even among the Japanese minis a regression of quality, shape and materials is evident when the bears are compared according to age. The earliest examples, c. 1920's, had narrow bodies that were well-defined. The last bears made around the late 1970's have fatter bellies, shorter, less distinctive necks, and plastic eyes and noses. The synthetic plush fabric is thicker and fuzzier and is glued on haphazardly with little care. (See Plate 185.)

Several Teddy-like styles of bears on all fours were also made in Japan. One company produced a series of hard-bodied animals with tape measures hidden inside. A red, oval paper tag sewn to the chest reads "I am a Tape Measure, Pull My Tail." The mini-bear version came in at least two sizes, 2½" (6.5 cm) and 2¾" (7 cm) high, and in an assortment of natural-looking fabric shades. (See Plates 186 – 189.)

A similar style of bear with a longer body was also available. These engaging examples were supplied with a squeaker in the body. Pressing the head and tail towards each other produces a high-pitched, playful noise. The characteristics of all the "bears on fours" are strikingly similar to the small, jointed versions, right down to the glued-on blue label marked "Made in Japan." It is probable that one manufacturer created the majority of these tiny Teddies. (See Plates 190 – 191.)

Periodically, other small bears appear on the market, which seem to be of Japanese origin, but conclusive proof remains elusive. In these cases where the original manufacturer may be impossible to document, the collector must be guided by instinct and intuition. Although some of these examples were made of mohair with sewn-on mouths and noses, the sparse, less expensive fabric and simpler methods of manufacture still indicate Japan. (See Plates 192 – 197.)

Tiny Teddies may also be found in an upright position with small stick-like arms outstretched to clasp a ball or baby bottle. Made in a similar manner to other Japanese Teds with plush fabric glued to a pressed fiber or wood body, these interesting examples came in several sizes and colors with glass and plastic eyes and noses. (See Plates 198 – 201.)

Celluloid, a trademark material made from nitrocellulose and camphor, was a favorite in the Japanese toy industry before plastic became readily available after WWII. Flammability was a serious defect intrinsic to this product and contributed to the eventual obsolescence of celluloid toys. Small, string-jointed bears in bright colors were molded in this inexpensive medium from the 1930's until the war when the raw materials became too difficult to obtain and then afterwards during the "Occupied Japan" period from the late 1940's through the early 1950's. (See Plates 202 – 203.)

Tape-measure Teddies were also available in celluloid in numerous shapes and colors. These bright little bears with their painted-on features are pert and expressive as well as practical. (See Plates 204 – 206.)

**PLATE 186**
At 2½" (6.5 cm) high, this light gold Teddy, c. 1930's, still sports his original red oval chest tag reading "I am a Tape Measure, Pull My Tail." The cloth tape marked "Japan" is encased in a metal container embedded into the bear's pressed fiber body. A blue paper label stuck to his belly also reads "Made in Japan." $75.00.

**PLATE 187**
This light brown tape measure Teddy is 2¾" (7 cm) high, and except for its larger size, is nearly identical to the previous example. A white, felt-like fabric makes the muzzle area appear more pronounced. $75.00.

**PLATE 188**
This light cinnamon colored Teddy tape measure is 2¾" (7 cm) high with an original blue rayon ribbon, amber glass eyes, and a black glass nose. $75.00.

**PLATE 189**
The style of this 2¾" (7 cm) dark cinnamon tape measure bear is unusual because of its super-large, cub-like ears, red-stitched floss nose, and upright sitting position. The tape is still located in the tail area, and a blue rayon ribbon adorns the neck. $95.00.

83

**PLATE 190**
Standing just 2¼" (5.5 cm) high, this gold plush bear on all fours had its delicate glass nose broken in the heat of play. Luckily, the blue "Made in Japan" label is present, and the sweet-sounding, spring mounted internal squeaker still works beautifully. $50.00.

**PLATE 191**
This light gold bear on all fours is 2¾" (7 cm) high with a glass nose and eyes and a pink rayon ribbon. The squeaker spring still compresses, but no sound is emitted. Teddy can talk no longer. $40.00.

**PLATE 192**
At 4" high this wire-jointed, excelsior-stuffed Ted of sparse gold mohair has amber glass eyes and a black floss nose. The one piece head and body construction and squat body style indicate he was made in Japan, c. 1920's. The 6½" (14.5 cm) high wooden "jigsaw construction" chair, "BABY" necklace, and c. 1920 mini book entitled *The Baby Bears and Christmas* are accessories added by the imaginative owner, Cindy Martin. Bear, $50.00; chair, $40.00; book, $35.00.

**PLATE 193**
Bright orange skimpy mohair and a matching satin ribbon give this 5" (12.5 cm) Teddy an original look. Excelsior stuffing, a one-piece head and body with wire-jointed limbs, amber glass eyes, and a black floss nose and mouth indicate this bear was made in Japan around 1930. This same style has also been seen in red and pink and is possibly the Japanese solution to competition from the brightly colored Schucos. $95.00. Private Collection.

**PLATE 194**
Measuring exactly 6" (15 cm) high, this wire-jointed, excelsior-stuffed Teddy is catching a few rays on his light tan mohair, now nearly worn away. The c. 1920's Ted with black glass eyes and remnants of a black floss nose, wears a striped cotton swimsuit with a coordinating blue cover-up and relaxes in his favorite wooden lounge chair. A jointed Teddy pendant just ¾" (2 cm) high in sterling silver adds the finishing touch. Bear, $125.00; chair, $25.00.

**PLATE 195**
This Teddy Baby-like bear is 5" (12.5 cm) high of bright gold mohair with a felt snout and feet that are similarly-styled to the popular Steiff original. This less expensive and less finely crafted bear with glass eyes and red ribbon and bell may be a Japanese look-alike, c. 1950's. $75.00. Private Collection.

**PLATE 196**
Sparse gold mohair and a one-piece head and body with a blue rayon ribbon and wire-jointed limbs imply this 3½" (9 cm) bear is probably from Japan, c. 1930's. $75.00. Private Collection.

**PLATE 197**
At 4½" (11.5 cm) high this gold mohair bear with large glass eyes looks decidedly feminine in her vintage, flower-trimmed hat (not original). She is most likely Japanese, c. 1940's. $75.00. Private Collection.

PLATE 198
The hard, pressed wood body and glued-on rayon plush indicate this 3" (9 cm) Ted is probably Japanese, c. 1950. The eyes and nose are plastic, and baby Ted holds a plastic milk bottle between two outstretched paws. $40.00.

PLATE 199
Orange-red rayon gives this 3" (9 cm), c. 1950 milk bottle bear with plastic nose and eyes a wild and wooly look. $50.00.

PLATE 200
At 2" (5 cm) high this papier-maché standing bear with glass eyes and green paper ball is likely an early, c. 1920's version of the upright bears. A pink rayon ribbon around his neck might've attached him to a pin or some larger object. $40.00.

PLATE 201
These two plush-covered upright Teds are later models, c. 1940's of the previous papier-maché bear. A blue rayon ribbon joins them together and attaches to a pin. The brown bear still carries his white paper ball, but his gold-colored companion has lost his little milk bottle along the way. $75.00 for the pair.

**PLATE 202**
The string joints on this 4" (10 cm) pink celluloid bear have come loose with age, and the molded "fur" is a bit faded, but the hot pink painted-on nose and mouth look as lively as ever. This late 1940's to early 1950's Teddy is marked "Japan" in ink on his right foot and the words "Made in Occupied Japan" are faintly molded onto his back. $40.00. Private Collection.

**PLATE 203**
"Foreign" is the word molded onto the back of this 2¼" (5.5 cm) yellow celluloid Teddy purchased in England. A cotton ribbon, string joints, red painted features, and paw pads add to his c. 1930's personality. $40.00. Private Collection.

88

**PLATE 204**
Standing 2¾" (7 cm) high from the bottom of his pink base to the top of his painted pink ears, this bright red celluloid Ted is marked "Made in Occupied Japan," conclusively dating his age from approximately 1948 to 1953. A sweet, endearing expression and a tape measure stored in the base add much to his cuteness and collectibility. $95.00.

**PLATE 205 (above right)**
This mint-green version of a tape-measure Teddy has textured "fur" molded into his form and a perky, upturned tail. The white painted hands and face with the pink tongue poking out give him a pouty expression. $95.00.

**PLATE 206**
A fleur-de-lis on the back of this 2¾" (7 cm) blue celluloid Teddy's neck may be a clue to the Japanese company that made him. The active, animated pose and wonderfully whimsical smile make his practical, tape measure base seem superfluous. This mischievous little bear's message is clear, encouraging any industrious sewer to put work away and "come out to play!" $95.00.

89

# Chapter Six

# Miscellaneous Miniatures

Many wonderful little bears fall into the "miscellaneous" category, not being readily identified to a specific manufacturer. Germany, in particular, has long been known for its outstanding toy industry, and a number of unusual small bears can be attributed to that country. Mohair, metal, plush, synthetics, ceramics, and celluloid were all used in the creation of these miniature German mascots, and their styles and functions are accordingly diverse. (See Plates 207 – 219.)

Other countries such as England, Austria, France, and the United States have produced vintage minis ranging from plastic bear banks to flocked perfume Teddies. These, too, were made in a myriad of materials, and often designed with an extra, practical function in mind. In this way, tiny Teds around the world have managed to make regular appearances in people's daily lives. (See Plates 220 – 232.)

Novelty, knick-knack type Teds can frequently be found in one form or another of bisque, porcelain, or ceramic. Some were made to double discreetly as pen-holders, pincushions, or salt-shakers, while others were simply fun and frivolous, their main purpose in life to sit amusingly upon a shelf and share their smiles. The majority of these breakable bears were produced in Japan or Germany from the beginning of the big bear craze (early 1900's) until the present. More recent examples are explored in Chapter Eight. (See Plates 233 – 246.)

**PLATE 207**
**This 2" (5 cm) green celluloid bear, stands on a red roly-poly base marked "Made in Germany," indicating a pre-WWII origin. He holds a matching green milk bottle and may have been part of a larger toy set. $45.00.**

**PLATE 208**
**At 4" (10 cm) and 3" (7.5 cm) high these hard-bodied bears with light brown rayon plush covering may at first appear to be of Japanese origin, but a paper label marked "Germany" confirms their c. 1930's German origin. $50.00 – $65.00 each. Courtesy D.A. Horton.**

**PLATE 209**
This 2½" (6.5 cm) German Teddy belongs to the same bear family pictured previously, except his hard, pressed fiber body is covered in a light, bright shade of gold. $50.00. Courtesy D.A. Horton.

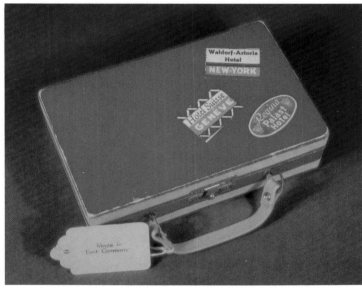

**PLATE 210**
Traveling stickers from exotic and glamorous destinations decorate the surface of this 5¼" (13 cm) red traveling trunk. The charming style and original paper tag marked "Made in East Germany" still attached to the handle, point to a mid-1950's beginning.

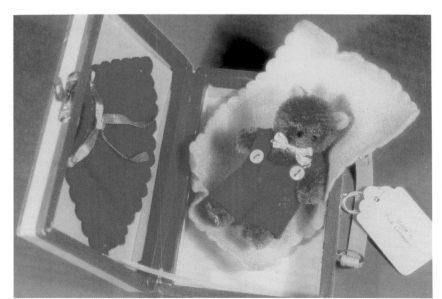

**PLATE 211**
The trunk opens to reveal its traveling treasure, a 3¼" (8 cm) brown mohair bear in red felt overalls with matching red cape, pink neck ribbon, pink felt inner ears, glass eyes, and wire-jointed limbs that move in unison. A sticker on the bottom of his right foot also reads "East Germany." Still sewn to his yellow felt blanket, this take-along Teddy has never been given a chance to play. $200.00. Private Collection.

PLATE 213
Standing 2½" (6.5 cm) long by 1½" (4 cm) high, this white bear on all fours is clearly the companion to the Teddy previously pictured. All details are identical except for the color of the fabric and the position of the pose. $50.00.

PLATE 212
This 2½" (6 cm) blue standing hardbodied bear is covered in a "loopy" rayon-type material with a shiny red and white ribbon, large black glass eyes, and felt inner ears. His origin is Germany, c. 1930's. $50.00.

PLATE 214
This 2" (5 cm) red and black metal convertible, c. 1920's from Germany, contains a man-driver, a bear riding behind, and a faithful dog perched at the front. $50.00. Private Collection.

PLATE 215
From the German Kohler company, this 4" (10 cm) mechanical bear, c. 1930, dances in a circle when wound. Felt ears are inserted into his lithographed metal body. $125.00.

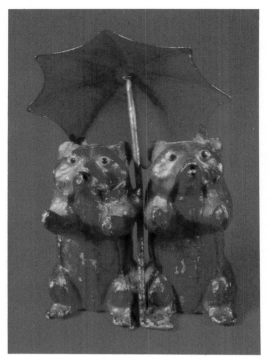

PLATE 216
"Tut, tut, it looks like rain..." Two non-pooh-like, c. 1930's painted metal Teddies 1¾" (4.5 cm) high from Germany share the protection of a red umbrella. $95.00. Courtesy Donna Harrison West.

PLATE 217
"Peep!" is the sound this quaint accordion-fold squeak toy makes when the colorful paper bottom is raised and lowered. A puff-ball bear of batting material clutches an opalescent egg with a batting chick visible inside (vintage flowers not original). This c. 1920's toy is possibly of German origin. $200.00. Private Collection.

PLATE 219
Surprise! Teddy's head pulls off to reveal a tiny German bisque doll disguised in bear costume. Are there any mischievous dolls dressed up in Teddy clothes whose owners remain unaware of their true identity? You can't really blame the dolls for being just a bit jealous. After all, the bears are getting so much attention... $250.00. Courtesy Sara Phillips.

PLATE 218
This 1¼" (3 cm) dark gold Teddy, c. 1920's is intricately hand-crocheted with a black embroidered nose and mouth (red vintage hat not original).

PLATE 220
These two 4" (10 cm) Teddies are old and new examples from the Austrian company of Berg. The c. 1950's bear at right is jointed and sewn of mohair. A green plastic chest button with the Berg name imprinted makes identification simple. The 1980's model at left is made of acrylic with a bendable body beneath. A red metal heart on the chest and a tag sewn into the leg are the contemporary forms of I.D. Newer bear, $35.00; vintage bear, $75.00. Private Collection.

PLATE 221
"Misha" the bear, the 1980 Olympic mascot was produced as a souvenir in several sizes, including this miniature 1¼" (3 cm) acrylic version made in Korea and mounted on a stickpin. The eyes and nose are plastic and a ribbon depicting the five olympic rings encircles his waist. An inexpensive but interesting little bear. $15.00.

PLATE 222
"The Three Little Bears" are pictured on this red, yellow and blue c. 1950's box by Kleeware. "Made in England" is stamped on the side along with the pertinent question, "Who's been eating my porridge?"

PLATE 223
The box opens to reveal Mother (3½"/9 cm), Father (4"/10 cm), and Baby (2½"/6.5 cm) bears in the form of blue and pink plastic rattles. Technically, these are not true Teddies, but Mother, who shows a bit of bosom beneath her apron, and Father, who sports a pipe, cane and bow-tie, are certainly more civilized than ferocious. Baby carries a white painted-on lollipop, and he is just right. $100.00 for the boxed set.

PLATE 224
"The Three Bears" make another appearance in plastic, this time in the form of a 4" (10 cm) yellow bank made in the U.S.A., c. 1950's. Three slots in the bear's backs make saving your pennies even easier. $30.00.

**PLATE 225**
Two Teddy twins, just 1" (2.5 cm) high, are suspended from a plastic bow brooch with yellow painted-on polka-dots. This whimsical piece is most likely British, c. 1940's. $25.00.

**PLATE 226**
Plastic Teddy charms like these 1960's bears from Hong Kong came in bright colors of green and yellow, ranging in size from 1¼" (3 cm) to 1½" (4 cm). Possible uses might have been for party favors or extra temptations in candy machines. $20.00 for the set of three.

PLATE 227
Smart manufacturers realized the potential power of the Teddy Bear to help promote their products. This 4½" (11.5 cm) flocked bear was a special item offered at Christmas around the 1960's or 1970's along with a tiny bottle of Max Factor perfume. What woman could resist this fancy, feminine bear with green jeweled eyes and a matching green satin ribbon? $25.00. Private Collection.

PLATE 228
Contemporary styling with a gold plastic head and frosted glass body distinguish this 3" (7.5 cm) bear bottle of Avon perfume from the 1970's. $30.00. Private Collection.

PLATE 229
An early 1900's whistle like this 2¼" (5.5 cm) version carved in pipe-stone clay is the perfect item to entertain with at a Teddy Bear's picnic. $85.00. Courtesy Donna Harrison West.

PLATE 230
Avon offered this 3½" (9 cm) high flocked glass Teddy bottle during the 1970's. The large head with airbrushed features unscrews to access the perfume inside. $25.00. Private Collection.

**PLATE 231**
A 2" (5 cm) high cut-out of a classic bear graces the front of this flat, Teddy-shaped celluloid pincushion. A thick pad of red felt between two flat bear layers provides a means for securing pins and needles.

**PLATE 232**
The back of the pincushion extorts the advantages of "Dyspepsia Compound" as prepared by C.S. Hanks, Corner Drug Store. This type of early 1900's item crosses collecting boundaries, appealing to bear, advertising and sewing accessory enthusiasts all at once. $110.00. Courtesy Anne Powell.

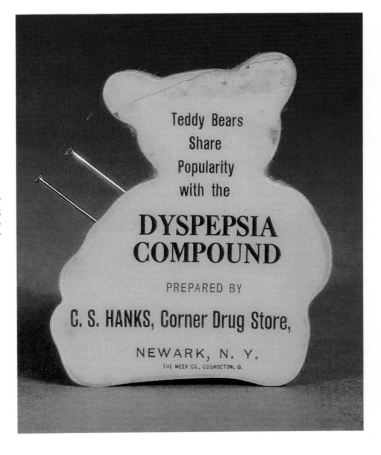

98

**PLATE 233**
A crocheted dress and handbag were original accessories found on this 2" (5 cm) German bisque girl-bear from Germany, c. 1910 – 1920. Many similar styles were available, including dressed boy-bears and other engaging animals. $250.00. Courtesy Donna Harrison West.

**PLATE 234**
Recent versions of the early bisque Teddies have been made like this 2¼" (5.5 cm) painted composition bear from the 1970's – 1980's with a crocheted dress of synthetic fibers. This type of Teddy should be purchased for its own merit, not as an antique original. $15.00. Private Collection.

PLATE 235
2½" (6.5 cm) panda buddies with painted-on features, pose for their picture. Inexpensive ceramic Teds like these were made in Japan, c. 1950. $10.00.

PLATE 236
These 2½" (6.5 cm) ceramic bears were designed as table-top salt and pepper shaker Teddies. The c. 1950's pair was fired with an attractive, caramel-colored glaze and rust-colored pads. $20.00. Private Collection.

PLATE 237
This 2½" (6 cm) violin-toting ceramic Teddy, marked Japan, will play his way into your heart. The blue googly eyes and fanciful expression appear to be in the 1930's style. $15.00.

PLATE 238
Clutching tightly on his white china jar (possibly an inkwell?) this 2½" (6.5 cm) glazed black bear of unknown origin makes a delightful desk-top guardian. $45.00. Courtesy Donna Harrison West.

**PLATE 239**
At 1¾" (4.5 cm) high, this yellow-glazed, googly-eyed, c. 1930's ceramic Ted is marked "Germany" on its back and bottom. Designed with a hollow, fabric stuffed head to be used as a pincushion, he is a cute and practical sewing companion. $85.00. Courtesy Anne Powell.

**PLATE 240**
These three Teddy friends from Japan, 3" (8 cm) high, look suspiciously similar to the previously pictured Ted from Germany. Toy manufacturers are notorious for "borrowing" ideas, and if a style proves successful it is likely to be copied sooner or later. These bear buddies also have holes in their heads, possibly for pincushions, or pencils, or...? $50.00.

**PLATE 241**
This simple, white ceramic bear, 2" (5 cm) sitting, from Japan, c. 1930's, was never an expensive item, but someone considered it dear enough to save all these years. $10.00.

**PLATE 242**
This 1¾" porcelain Teddy from the early 1900's has holes punched into its base in the manner of porcelain dresser dolls. A powder-puff, pincushion, or other useful item could be sewn to it, and the finely-detailed little bear would be used as the handle — a rare and interesting example. $95.00. Courtesy D.A. Horton.

**PLATE 243**
This 1½" (4 cm), c. 1920 bisque snow-baby bear has a rough, textured "fur" body, a blue ribbon around his neck and a smoothly sculpted face and paws. Like the sought-after snow-baby children, he is probably of German origin. $50.00.

**PLATE 244**
Snow-baby type bears were also made in Japan, such as this 1¾" (4.5 cm), c. 1920's, bisque example which is more of a polar bear than a true Teddy style. $30.00. Private Collection.

**PLATE 245**
A 3" (7.5 cm) green glazed porcelain purse is the perfect size to tote the two Teddy figurines inside. This is just one example of a series of bears (and other animals) from the early 1900's which accessorized everything from cars and binoculars to jars and boxes made of the same green-glazed material. The bears are nearly always the same style, with outstretched paws, either in a standing or sitting position. $95.00.

**PLATE 246**
Pink and blue glazing with large black eyes and nose give this 2½" (6 cm) ceramic Teddy, made in Occupied Japan, a sweet, stylized look. $25.00.

Miniature bears did patriotic duty during the presidential campaign of 1905. Their high-powered namesake, Theodore Roosevelt, was up for re-election and "Teddy's Bear's" served as the perfect promotional item. Tiny Teds were turned into miniature mascots for the popular personality whose name had become synonymous with the stuffed bear. Roosevelt's close association with America's best-loved toy was put to good use by savvy supporters who wore miniature bears in the form of badges, buttons, and stick-pins.

The campaign badge bear was produced in a simple style of white or gold chenille with hard paper paw pads, metal claws and nose, and glass bead eyes. Some were wire-jointed at the arms and legs, others merely poseable by means of a wire embedded inside the chenille. Many do not retain their original ribbons, buttons, or badges, and since some have been recently added by dealers or collectors, it is often difficult to determine what is original to the item and what is not.

After observing the enthusiastic profusion of political memorabilia at a recent presidential campaign, it is easy to imagine that the original badge-wearers must have added their own assortment of red, white, and blue ribbons or Roosevelt buttons to their tiny Teddy Bears. Picturing a crowd of Roosevelt supporters all wearing their campaign bears is enough to make any mini-collector equally enthusiastic!

These little bears are highly sought after today, not just by Teddy bear collectors but by political collectors as well. (See Plates 247 – 250.)

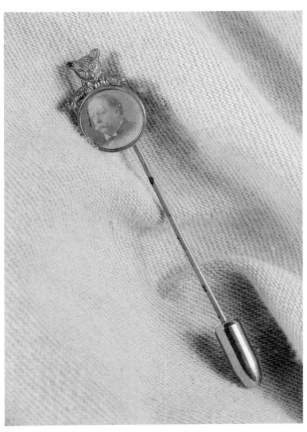

**PLATE 247**
**This rare stickpin, c. 1904, contains a ½" (1 mm) diameter photo of president Roosevelt. Behind the picture, which was probably worn for political support, is a brass-colored miniature metal bear with outstretched arms and legs. $95.00.**

**PLATE 248**
**This rare 3½" (9 cm) campaign bear, c. 1904, is dressed up in Teddy Roosevelt rough rider costume. The paper hat and belt, black composition boots, and patriotic bow tie, all original, give the tan chenille bear a cute, but decidedly comical, "rough and ready" look. $400.00 up. Private Collection.**

**PLATE 249**
This 3½" (9 cm) badge bear was worn by a Teddy Roosevelt supporter during the 1904 re-election campaign. The bear is made of a super-fluffy chenille (pipe-cleaner) type material with glass bead eyes, a metal nose and claws, and glued-on paper paw pads. It was probably attached at one time to a wide badge-type ribbon and campaign button. $275.00.

**PLATE 250**
A vintage ribbon and Teddy Roosevelt button were added to this 3½" (9 cm) jointed campaign badge bear, c. 1904. An amazing amount of realism was achieved with these early, inexpensively-made bears. $300.00 with button. Private Collection.

# Chapter Seven

# Uptown Teddies —
## Gold, Silver and Other Elegant Bear Accessories

Since Teddy's early days, miniature bears have ventured beyond the realm of childhood and graduated into the adult world as fashionable ornaments, accentuating everyday trinkets from brooches to button-hooks, seals, salt-shakers and chatelaines. Many non-toy makers exploited the bullish Teddy bear market, producing precious bear marvels in sterling silver and gleaming gold.

British silversmiths led the field in this area, and luckily most of these marvelous miniatures were hall-marked; so, a magnifying glass and a bit of research can uncover accurate information about the precise date and locale in which they were made. Most of these silver minis were crafted around 1910, when the first Teddy bear craze was in full swing.

Silver bears may not be as cuddly as their furry, sometimes stuffed counterparts, but they have a certain beauty that comes with the patina of age, and some of their fascination lies in speculating about the adults who owned them. Imagine your Edwardian friend is visiting for the afternoon. As you sit chatting, bent over some fine embroidery, she shows off her brand new silver pincushion. It's very modern, the rage of the day — a fully-jointed Teddy bear, of course!

The little bear was an anniversary gift from her husband. And what did she buy him? A silver Teddy bear seal with his initials carved in the gemstone base. How exquisite!

That possible past scenario makes one realize just how far "bear mania" had spread. It also makes me wonder if any English aristocrats really used their tiny British bears to seal important documents. Hmmm... (See Plates 251 – 256.)

**PLATE 251**
A 1" (2.5 cm) high Teddy, c. 1909 from Birmingham, England, sits atop his silver pincushion throne. This same sitting bear was used to decorate many other everyday objects and accessories. $400.00. Courtesy Anne Powell.

**PLATE 252**
The hallmark on this 1¾" (4.5 cm) jointed silver muzzle bear shows it was crafted in Birmingham, England, c. 1908 – 1909. A hard, cloth-covered pincushion on its back made it useful as a sewing tool, and the ring on the head may have attached it to a cord, neck-chain, or chatelaine. Tiny glass or gemstone eyes are missing from this model, which is otherwise in excellent condition, considering the fragile, fur-textured arms and legs are hollow. This same style of bear was also made in a slightly larger size. $1,300.00 up. Courtesy Anne Powell.

**PLATE 253**
This 1¾" (4.5 cm) muzzle bear look-alike, recreated by Dottie Ayers, is actually a fine and more reasonably-priced reproduction of the bear pictured in Plate 252. Unlike the English original, this Ted is made in solid silver or gold, giving it extra strength and durability — a sapphire- or ruby-eyed treasure to enjoy for generations. $285.00.

**PLATE 254**
Here the 1" (2.5 cm) silver bear seen in Plate 251 becomes a tiny Teddy seal on a base of bloodstone chalcedony, suitable for engraving with the family crest or monogram. $250.00.

**PLATE 255**
Golden glass eyes and a hinged head with hollow body are the identifying features of this 2⅛" (5 cm) reproduction Teddy. The early 1900's model might have been used as a match safe or other type of trinket container. $200.00. Courtesy Donna Harrison West.

**PLATE 256**
The 1909 small sitting bear from Birmingham is pictured here as part of a buttonhook handle. Many-buttoned boots and gloves were de rigeur in those days for fashionably dressed women who had never heard of velcro. A handsome hook like this was necessary to speed-up the daily dressing ordeal. $275.00. Courtesy Anne Powell.

The child of the house was not neglected, of course. Silver Teddy rattles, pacifier tops, and teething rings were abundant in the 1910 era. Rather than being born with a silver spoon in their mouths, privileged Edwardian Tots had the opportunity to chew on a better status symbol of the day — small silver bears. What those poor bears must have gone through! Luckier Teddies were hung safely around the necks of English Nannies. (See Plates 257 – 264.)

**PLATE 257 (left above)**
Double-sided bears like this c. 1909 (1¼"/3 cm) silver example were usually parts from pacifier tops, serving nursery-room duty as small nanny's aids. The original glass or gemstone eyes were often lost, hopefully in the crib or cradle, rather than down some little dear's throat. $75.00. Courtesy Donna Harrison West.

**PLATE 258 (left below)**
No mark of origin can be found on this ¾" (2 cm) clown-bear rattle attached to a small, celluloid ring. A ruff around Ted's neck and a squat, sitting body give him a later, more stylized look. $45.00. Courtesy Donna Harrison West.

**PLATE 259**
A mother-of-pearl handle allowed baby or his nursemaid to hold this fine double-sided silver rattle, c. 1910. Bells on either side added extra interest and play value to the 2" (5 cm) high British-made bear (measured minus the handle). $350.00. Courtesy Donna Harrison West.

**PLATE 260**
1914 is the approximate birth-date for this 2¼" (5.5 cm) silver bear. When the current owner adopted him, the bell wasn't working, and Teddy had lost his capacity to rattle. On closer examination, she discovered that the hollow base was stuffed with small wisps of fine wool, which, when removed, allowed the bell to sound freely. Perhaps the first young owner was afraid of the noise. Or maybe Mother had grown tired of hearing her over-playful child making Teddy "talk" and cleverly managed to maintain her own peace and quiet! $250.00. Private Collection.

**PLATE 261**
A larger (1½"/4 cm) sitting bear was also made by Birmingham silversmiths around 1909, and this type of Ted found usefulness in many forms. He's pictured here as a child's bell-adorned rattle, attached to a handle made in mother-of-pearl. $400.00. Courtesy Donna Harrison West.

**PLATE 262**
A powder-shaker with removable head is slightly larger (2"/5 cm) than the bear previously pictured but must have been styled by the same Birmingham silversmiths, c. 1909. $400.00. Courtesy Donna Harrison West.

**PLATE 263**
The 1½" (4 cm) style is shown here again without the handle or bells. It is possible that those pieces have been subsequently removed but just as likely that the same bear was produced in different ways. $300.00. Private Collection.

**PLATE 264**
Teddy treasures may be hiding in your grandmother's sewing box. Search for any of these brass bear buttons, ½" (1 cm) to ¾" (2 cm) used to decorate children's mohair coats in the early 1900's. Kids weren't content to merely own their bears, they wanted to dress like Teddy, too. $40.00 – $50.00 each.

Searching for Teddy bear charms in silver or gold can become a collecting challenge in itself. From the early 1900's to the present, metal Teddy talismans, suitable for hanging from a bracelet or necklace, have been produced by insightful companies and artisans who know there's no better way to take Teddy along with you than to pull or pin him on. Wearing your bear helps safeguard against loss and prevents any possible emotional trauma from separation.

Contemporary collectors need their portable jewelry bears more than ever, and many aren't willing to stop at only one. If a single tiny Ted can help you through the day, two, five, or ten Teddy tokens may be the bearers of even greater good fortune. The "charming" Teddy necklaces pictured below represent the more is merrier philosophy. (See Plates 265 – 268.)

**PLATE 265**
This golden assortment of bears (and some bunnies) is a coveted collection of items old and new, carefully acquired. Shopping with this theme in mind can be time-consuming, but surprisingly simple — just buy more gold bears! $2,500.00 for all. Courtesy Donna Harrison West.

**PLATE 266**
Creativity may be called upon when deciding how to arrange one's treasured Teddy necklace. A 2¼" (5.5 cm) Avon perfume bear locket from the 1970's is the central focus of this all-bear charm necklace. $200.00. Private Collection.

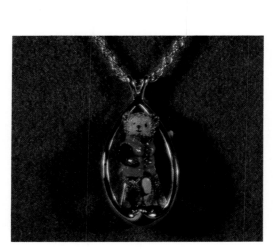

**PLATE 267**
Robert Olszewski, master miniaturist, sculpted this ¾" (2 cm) Camper Bialosky Bear for Goebel in 1986. The exquisitely hand-painted bronze Teddy is set in a vermeil teardrop-shaped mounting and was elegantly gift-boxed with its own necklace or necktie chain. "Never be without him" suggested an original advertisement. Re-sale $200.00 up.

**PLATE 268**
Buying silver bears wherever you go can be an excellent, and relatively inexpensive way to satisfy a craving for tiny Teds. If you keep at it, the end result may look something like this marvelous melange. $2,000.00 for all. Courtesy Donna Harrison West.

111

Modern designers have carried on the tradition of gold or glittery bear wear with even greater style and imagination. Butler and Wilson, British jewelers of some renown, offer rhinestone bedecked bear bracelets and brooches in limited editions. Tiffany makes a fine silver rattle for contemporary kiddies, and several other jewelry makers have come out with tiny sculptured Teds (for deserving mothers) that look especially sweet in solid gold.

Judith Leiber, a handbag designer extraordinaire, whose wonderful work has been featured in the New York Museum of Modern Art, has created the ultimate in take-along Teddy luxury. Her elegant, beaded bear evening purses and jewel-paved pillboxes simply shimmer with sparkling, multicolored crystals. So who says bears aren't glamorous? (See Plates 269 – 274.)

**PLATE 269**
British jewelers, Butler and Wilson made this limited edition bracelet in 1991, with alternating links of gold-toned and rhinestone-studded ¾" (2 cm) Teddies. $150.00. Courtesy Donna Harrison West.

**PLATE 270**
Costume jewelry collectors had an opportunity to buy their own bit of bear-wear when Butler and Wilson produced this limited edition, 1¾" (4.5 cm) bear brooch in 1991. $50.00. Courtesy Donna Harrison West.

**PLATE 271**
Solid, gleaming gold is the metal of choice for beautiful jewelry bears like these, ranging in size from ¾" (2 cm) to 1" (2.5 cm). Many modern jewelers have tried their hand at contemporary Teddy creations like these, knowing no woman could resist such tantalizing bear temptations. Left to right – $400.00, $600.00, $500.00. Courtesy Donna Harrison West.

**PLATE 272**
To be on the cutting edge of current Teddy style, try these Gummi-bear earrings on for size. You'll have to look elsewhere if your sweet-tooth suddenly strikes, because these colorful Teds are made of plastic, not candy. $65.00.

**PLATE 273**
Where can you find this fabulous, highly fashionable bear key-chain? At the finest department stores only, from Judith Leiber, of course. The 1⅛" (3 cm) golden bear wears a sculpted-on jacket with a ruby-colored cabochon clasp and is so beary chic! $80.00.

**PLATE 274**
The most dazzling miniature bears ever made are the 1¾" (4.5 cm) pillbox and 5" (12.5 cm) minaudiere by Judith Leiber. Sweetness and sophistication are combined in a sparkling, multi-colored costume of Austrian crystals. This perfect bear purse has a built-in shoulder chain, and opens to reveal two compartments, which contain a custom comb, mirror, and golden leather change purse. Never has it been so enjoyable and appropriate to bring your Teddy to a favorite opera, ballet, or the latest Broadway opening. Pillbox, $335.00; purse, $2,895.00. Prices may vary on certain designs. Courtesy Judith Leiber. Advertising art from Peter Rogers Associates; Dennis Blachut, photographer.

# Chapter Eight

# Contemporary Teddies, Manufactured

Miniature bear-making is still going strong in the 1990's. Ninety years since the first Teddy hugged his way into a child's heart, bears are as beloved as ever, and tiny Teds are being made in profusion. Searching for the modern miniature can be as rewarding as the hunt for vintage bears, since the variety and selection is even better.

With production size and the company's reputation as additional factors for the collector's consideration, contemporary Teds should meet the same criteria of quality and cuteness as their early ancestors. Or, the buying decision may be based simply on the bear's power to bring pleasure or beauty to the owner's life with little regard given to future investment potential.

Still, there can be some degree of excitement in trying to predict the future. What early bear buyer would have believed that a tiny child's toy, purchased for less than a dollar in the not too distant past, would be worth several hundred times that amount today? A common collector's fantasy is to travel back in a time machine and purchase treasures from the past in their boxed and untouched state.

Think of it, a sort of dream bear vacation where your wildest Teddy fantasies could come true. How about a few dozen Steiff ornament bears for your Christmas tree? They cost about a dollar apiece in the 1920's. Or maybe a boxed set of blue Schucos? Or a complete compact collection, currently available from your local toy store.

Will collectors a hundred years from now be searching for the same things, or will Teds from our era be highly valued as well? The answer to that question is where the challenge lies. Who knows what trinkets of today will become the greatest Teddy Bear treasures of tomorrow? (See Plate 275.)

Some future contenders for this honor are illustrated in the following photographs. Porcelain, glass, enamel, and bronze bears are currently made by high-end manufacturers who normally specialize in other items. Teddies have a way of sneaking into these otherwise exclusive inventories and making their appearance known. Herend, Daum, and Halcyon Days are just a few companies now producing bears that collecting connoisseurs consider worthy of name-dropping. (See Plates 276 – 283.)

Peter Fagan of Scotland is a current master of miniature bear manufacturing with his original

**PLATE 275**
**Rare Gummy Bears? Can any collector truly predict what items will have value in the future? Chances are, it could be something that we enjoy today and don't think about saving for tomorrow. Before you rush to the nearest candy store, consider this — will they still be sweet and chewy in a hundred years?**

Teddy Bear Collection from Colour Box Miniatures. Peter sculpts his designs in plasticine, often miniaturizing his ideas from older bear models which are full-sized. Molds are made from his prototype and each carefully-cast Teddy that emerges is hand-finished and painted to exactly match the original. The resulting bears are so finely detailed and full of personality that it's easy to see why the Fagan's creations enjoy world-wide success.

A short story written by Frances Fagan usually accompanies each individually-boxed bear, so the eventual owner knows Teddy's proper name and provenance. A collector's club with magazines, Christmas cards, special promotions, and an opportunity to attend the annual Colour Box Fair makes acquiring these small sculptures even more fun. (See Plates 284 – 287.)

**PLATE 276**
The Herend company of Hungary is known for its fine china, but this 4" (10 cm) blue-patterned porcelain bear with 24 karat gold trim beats a four piece place-setting any day. $275.00. Private Collection.

**PLATE 277**
Daum Crystal of France creates bear drama with this 4" (10 cm) signed Teddy of clear leaded glass. $175.00.

**PLATE 278**
From the Crystal Zoo comes this fine pair of faceted bears ¾" (2 cm) and 1¾" (4.5 cm) high. Assembled from cut shapes of Austrian crystal, they have a beautiful ability to catch and diffuse spectral colors. $25.00 – $35.00.

**PLATE 279**
Halcyon Days English enamels produced this 2" (5 cm) porcelain Teddy Bear seal in the late 1980's. Inspired by the 18th century Chelsea miniatures, this Teddy and her pink cushion were delicately hand-painted, then set in a gold-plated silver mount with a pink rhodonite stone at the base. $250.00. Private Collection.

**PLATE 280**
The 2" (5 cm) porcelain seal bear is also shown here in blue. Private Collection.

117

**PLATE 281**
This solid-bronze figurine, just 1" (2.5 cm) high, was cast by the Bermann Bronze Works in Vienna, Austria, in the same manner as the early Viennese miniatures, then hand-painted in shades of gold and Teddy Bear brown. $150.00. Private Collection.

**PLATE 282**
Here a 1" (2.5 cm) high Bermann-made bear sits on a small red heart of solid bronze. Since each small sculpture is painstakingly decorated by hand, every one projects a slightly different personality. $150.00.

**PLATE 283**
Looks like Teddy beddy time for this 1" (2.5 cm) Bermann bronze bear in a red nightcap. He does look a bit sleepy sitting atop his blue, star-painted cushion with gold-tassel trim. $150.00. Private Collection.

**PLATE 284**
Colour Box miniatures by Peter Fagan come in individual boxes, each with an accompanying story. These 1½" (4 cm) to 2" (5 cm) examples are all cleverly modeled after larger antique Teddies. $10.00 – $20.00 each.

**PLATE 285**
"Captain Arthur Crown" (3¾"/9.5 cm) left, "Ben" (1¼"/3 cm) center, and "Damien" (2¾"/7 cm) right, are just a few of the imaginative creations from Colour Box miniatures. The names are picked to suit each Ted's personality and an accompanying miniature brochure gives the "bear facts" about their characters. $10.00 – $50.00 each.

**PLATE 286**
"Prudence" (2¾"/7 cm) left, loves to garden, "Binkie" (1¼"/3 cm) started life as a fairground prize, "Davey" (1¼"/3 cm) dreams of being big, "Arabella" (2¾"/7 cm), far right, is passionate and romantic, and "Grandma Rosie" (3"/7.5 cm) back center, loves hats. Grandma's back is turned so we can observe the numerous trinkets attached to her "best hat in the universe." All were created by Peter and Frances Fagan of Colour Box. $10.00 – $50.00 each.

**PLATE 287**
These Colour Box bears, 1¼" (3 cm) to 2" (5 cm), have all gathered round the honey jar while posing for pictures. The casting and painting process used by Peter Fagan allows for the tiny Teds to be reproduced in cute and incredible detail. Individually sculpted "stitches" can be seen on some models, but all are crafted with charm and charisma. $10.00 – $20.00 each.

Paddington Bear has been reproduced in miniature from his original storybook form by Eden Toys of Korea, and Coalport, an English china manufacturer has perfected him in porcelain. Other, less well-known bears abound in small, statue-like shapes of ceramic or plastic. (See Plates 288 – 293.)

Soft sculptured bears are currently made in miniature by companies like Clemens or Hermann, and some contemporary cottage-industries still create tiny Teds in the Schuco style, with a fuzzy fur covering applied to a durable metal body. The use of modern materials helps distinguish these from the earlier miniatures, originally conceived by Heinrich Müller. (See Plates 294 – 302.)

The photographs shown are just a small sampling of what's currently (or recently) available. Now it's up to you to find the rest!

**PLATE 288**
This 5" (12.5 cm) porcelain Paddington was purchased at Harrod's during the 1980's and is made by the British company of Coalport. $45.00. Courtesy Carol Porter.

**PLATE 289**
"Please look after this bear, Thank you" is the endearing note written on these two (3"/8 cm and 1½"/4 cm) Paddington bears from Eden Toys of Korea. The larger bear of plush wears a bright yellow hat, shiny raincoat, and red rubber boots. The baby version made in 1978, has a pliable rubber body with flocking on top, a maroon velveteen coat and a lemon yellow hat. Large, $8.00; small, $5.00.

**PLATE 290**
This 5" (12.5 cm) Lady bear resting comfortably on a park bench is a ceramic statue from Goebel, produced during the 1980's. $45.00. Courtesy Carol Porter.

**PLATE 291**
Lynn Ayers of England created this 3" (7.5 cm) scene of ceramic bears dancing merrily along, most likely on their way to the Teddy Bear's picnic. $115.00. Courtesy Donna Harrison West.

**PLATE 292**
Bears take to the highway in their 5" (12.5 cm) long ceramic convertible car.
Mom and Dad keep vigil up front while the cubs cavort in back. This lively holi-
day outing was made in 1990 by Lynn Ayers of England. $135.00. Courtesy
Donna Harrison West.

**PLATE 293**
This 1988 Lucy Rigg Christmas ornament from Enesco features a 1¾" (4.5 cm) Teddy
playing in an overstuffed trunk of plastic toys. Collecting ornament bears may become
a favorite Holiday tradition, as many different manufacturers make them, and new
designs become available each year. $35.00.

**PLATE 294**
"Hermann Teddy Original, Made in West Germany" is inscribed on the arm tag of this 5" (12.5 cm) orange-gold bear with glass eyes, c. 1980's. $60.00. Private Collection.

**PLATE 295**
This 5" (12.5 cm) Hermann Teddy, fully jointed with glass eyes and original tags still attached, was made especially for the 1988 Seattle bear convention. $75.00. Private Collection.

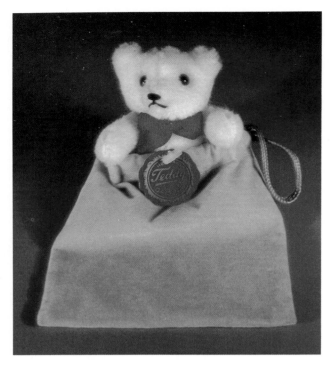

PLATE 296
This 4" (10 cm) white acrylic bendable-bodied bear by Hermann, c. 1980's, comes in his own velvet pouch for easy portability. $35.00. Private Collection.

PLATE 297
The lederhosen were made by an indulgent owner and are not original to this 3½" (9 cm) brown acrylic bear with plastic nose and eyes from Shackman, c. 1980's. $25.00. Private Collection.

PLATE 298
Clemens Spieltiere is the toy company that made this 4" (10 cm) fully jointed bear of lighter-tipped caramel mohair, c. 1980's. $40.00. Private Collection.

**PLATE 299**
This 3½" (9 cm) flocked bear, c. 1980's, has bendable arms and legs and is dressed in a darling felt and cotton costume, completely coordinated right down to his little black shoes. A tag applied to the back of his head reads "Handwork-Kunstlerschutz – West Germany." $35.00. Private Collection.

**PLATE 300**
This 2¾" (7 cm) "Berliner Bear" is made by Martin Weiss of West Germany in the same manner as the older Schuco minis. It is meant to be sold as a souvenir or reproduction and should not be confused with Schuco-made mohair bears of a similar style from the early 1970's. Check for the plastic eyes and nose and acrylic/cotton fur which is not found on previous bears by Schreyer and Co. A plain brown version is also currently produced. $20.00.

**PLATE 301**
Müller's idea for making miniature bears with a metal body was too good to be lost when Schuco closed its doors in the mid-1970's. Luckily, some small bears are still being made in the same way, and this 2¾" (7 cm) panda from Martin Weiss is such an example. The acrylic fur and plastic eyes clearly indicate that it's not an older Schuco. Otherwise, the construction is exactly the same. $18.00.

**PLATE 302**
These 2¾" (7 cm) bears were also made in the Schuco style but in colors quite different from Schreyer originals. The bear at left was made to commemorate the unification of Germany, and the colors are symbolic of the German flag. A tag at the bear's back reads "3 Okt. 1990, Heike-Bar, Nr. 475." Five hundred of these acrylic bears were made and, because of their historic association, are likely to become even more treasured with time. The bear at right sports a racy red acrylic coat with black ears, eyes and nose. Unification bear, $60.00; red bear, $20.00. Private Collection.

# Chapter Nine

# Contemporary Artist Bears

Concurrent with the renewed interest in vintage bears is a growing demand for new, artist-made miniatures. The market for small antique Teddies is large compared to a woefully limited supply of surviving specimens. The wait for one's dream bear can be long and frustrating, and if the perfect Teddy ever does turn up, the price may still keep the bear out of reach. So what can a collector do? Buy artist bears!

Of course, miniature artist-made Teddies can be equally elusive. The work of most mini-bear makers is in great demand because each creation must be slowly sewn by hand, usually taking longer to produce than a large bear, and sometimes requiring greater skill. Naturally, the number of bears that can be made is low, and the interest in these tiny Teddy sculptures is consequently high.

Although certainly not primitive, miniature bear-making can be considered a contemporary form of American folk art. The work is usually completed at home, in front of our favorite industrialized icon (the television), and the subject is a particularly appropriate symbol for our times. The size of the work is a further reflection of current cultural trends — shrinking space and a growing trend toward specialization.

Many hand-made minis are basic bears — simple, scaled-down versions of larger, sometimes antique Teddies. Others are directly inspired by a coveted vintage bear which is somehow out of reach. Small dressed or elaborately costumed bears are also available, and their diminutive size still does not diminish the quality or detail of their clothes.

Holidays are another favorite theme among mini-bear artists as Teddies tend to be linked with happy times. Bedtime bears are a popular design — who hasn't taken a Ted to bed? Fantasy bears also abound with fabulous winged or wild woodland forms that bring little bears even further into the land of make-believe.

The creativity and craftsmanship of these hand-made miniatures certainly exceeds that of any manufactured piece from the past. Assembling any small bear, including those that are company made, involves some degree of hand work or sewing, but the proficiency and finesse of today's best mini-bear makers is unprecedented. Only through years of practice can an artist gain such deftness with a needle and thread.

The result? Many of today's mini-creations are so lifelike, and the stitches that form them so neat and small, it's difficult to imagine they were sewn by human hands. It seems far more likely that they were made by magic.

Following are photos of bears made by many of today's top artists. Some specialize in miniatures, while others prefer to make Teddies both large and small. Many of the tiny Teds pictured are super-scarce, only one or a few of a kind that reside in private collections. Some are perfect prototypes that still live with the artists themselves.

The examples shown are not comprehensive, since many new and talented Teddy-makers continue to enter the market. Instead, these rarely-seen bears were carefully selected to give you an idea of the delightful diversity of styles and the energetic imaginations that go into the making of little bears.

**PLATE 303**
**Basic bears come in many colors, like this sampling of soft plush Teddies by Octavia Chin, ranging in size from 1¾" (4.5 cm) to 3¼" (8 cm). Most artists develop a certain style, and the bears they make are easily identifiable by that "look." After some experience in the field, it's possible to connect an artist with her creations simply by sight. $95.00 – $125.00. Private Collection.**

Note: Values given are approximate, and are not estimates of what the bears would bring on the re-sale market, rather they reflect current prices that the artists would charge to make similar Teddies today.

**PLATE 304**
Regina Brock made the 3" (7.5 cm) cream-colored bear shown here from hand-dyed mohair rovings, individually inserted into a padded metal armature. The resulting bear is an extra-soft blend of natural fibers with a sweet, very individual expression. Glass eyes and felt paw pads complete the classic details of this timeless Teddy. $350.00. Courtesy Carol Porter.

**PLATE 305**
"Timmy" is the name of this 6" (15 cm) gold mohair bear by Barbara Conley. He is fully-jointed with fine, traditional styling, wool felt pads, glass eyes and a custom-collar. This particular Ted is limited to an edition of ten. $145.00.

**PLATE 306**
Gail Silversmith has captured a wise and winsome expression in the eyes of these 3¼" (8 cm) hand-sewn bears. "Winston," wearing a pink silk bow, poses politely for the photo, while his gold basic bear buddy stands patiently behind. $140.00 each.

**PLATE 307**
Cindy Martin, well-known for her larger bears, also makes terrific, "Tiny Yesterbears" like these two sharing a c. 1900 child's size teacup (note the girls playing with their bear). The 3¼" (8 cm) gold mohair bear with leather pads (at left) is the artist's 1985 prototype for an edition of less than 50. The brown acrylic companion is 3" (7.5 cm) high with glass bead eyes and a needle-sculpted face. Acrylic, $150.00; mohair, $200.00.

PLATE 308
Tammie Lawrence made this 5" (12.5 cm) mohair "Ted" (at back) especially for this book. She normally makes only bigger bears, but has recently decided to give the smaller guys a try. A cuddly body and "take me home" face are the loveable results. $180.00. Emily Farmer's 3" (7.5 cm) "Murphy" (in front) was made in a limited edition of ten, with a wide head and pronounced hump to achieve the early bear look. The paw pads are of synthetic suede, and the body was skillfully assembled from a car seat cover! $105.00.

PLATE 309
White mohair gives this 3¼" (7.5 cm) Tiny Yesterbear by Cindy Martin a clean, classic look. The deep-set glass eyes and wide, silk floss nose add to his irresistible appeal. $200.00. Private Collection.

PLATE 310
Blueberries are a particular favorite of this 2¼" (5.5 cm) northeastern black bear, as seen by the mischievous look on his face and telltale blue stains on his snout. April Whitcomb Gustafson hand-sculpted this remarkably realistic Teddy from a clay compound, then covered the finished form in velvet and painted on the final touches with a true artist's eye. $250.00.

**PLATE 311**
This 2¼" (5.5 cm) Teddy by Odette Conley has long, narrow limbs, a large hump, and a traditional, triangular-shaped head, giving him the old-time aspect of early bears. What a perfect accessory for your doll house attic, along with this 1¼" (3 cm) Tiggy Winkle trunk. Bear, $110.00; trunk, $90.00.

**PLATE 312**
Anita Oliver of England has been making miniature bears since 1980, and her fine craftsmanship shows in these three Teds gathered in a 2" (5 cm) wooden bucket by Carol Rowland. Anita's bears are of gold and brown textured plush, 2½" (6.5 cm) and 1½" (4 cm) fully jointed, with orange and black embroidered eyes. Bears, $110.00 – $125.00; bucket, $10.00.

PLATE 313
Diane Turbarg's sparse mohair bear, 2½" (6.5 cm), is c. 1992, but the close-shaved fabric lends an illusion that Teddy is already much-loved. A 2" (5 cm) riding elephant, also by Diane, was inspired by Edwardian era riding toys. Bear, $80.00; elephant, $75.00.

PLATE 314
Worn and torn Teddies by Gail Silversmith look as though they've shared exciting lives. These 3¼" (8 cm) endearingly imperfect bears are made of soft synthetic fur, purposely repaired in strategic places. $150.00 each.

131

**PLATE 315**
"Ely" is a 4" (10 cm) mohair bear with personality plus, by Julie Van Houten-Lingle. The searching expression and artistically "antiqued" mohair add amazing character and charm. $175.00. Courtesy Carol Porter.

**PLATE 316**
Cathy Levy's little bears 1¾" (4.5 cm) and 2¼" (5.5 cm) are especially sweet and expressive for their size. Individually embroidered paw pads and cute, close-set glass eyes exemplify Cathy's current style. $135.00 – $150.00 each. Courtesy Leisa Masters.

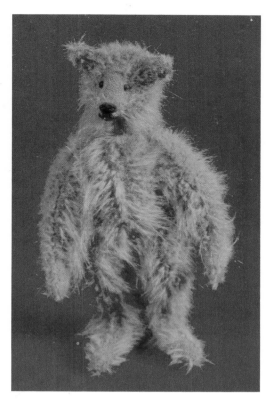

**PLATE 317**
"Tinkerbear" was the first miniature bear made by Carol-Lynn Rössel Waugh, in 1989. The 2½" (6.5 cm) fully-jointed Teddy was created in the same style as Carol-Lynn's larger bears and made as a special birthday surprise for daughter, Jenny-Lynn. $175.00.

**PLATE 318**
"Little Pank" by Steve Van Houten is 4½" (11.5 cm) of old rose mohair, specially shaved to show off a strong, and very original shape. Steve is well-known and admired for his larger bears, and this small example of his work, a unique and charismatic little bear, has an extra bit of animal about him and the rough and tumble impact of a decidedly boyish toy. $150.00. Courtesy Karen Thompson.

**PLATE 319**
Margaret Alford of England made these two miniature Teds in the early 1980's. The 1¾" bear at left is made of gold velvet plush over a hard, jointed body with leather pads, black embroidered eyes, nose and mouth. The ½" (1.5 cm) bear at right was designed to sit inside his own hazelnut house lined with velvet paper and hand-painted with flowers. $50.00 – $75.00 each. Private Collection.

**PLATE 320**
Lisa Lloyd's 2½" (6.5 cm) "Rachel" comes with her own 1¼" (3 cm) jointed cat named "Skyler." The gray plush bear wears blue silk bows and a blue calico collar, and kitty has coordinating rhinestone eyes. $250.00. Private Collection.

**PLATE 321**
This divine bear pair, one-of-a-kind, by artist Sara Phillips was inspired by her love of certain antique Teddy styles. The 1¼" (3 cm) cream-colored set consists of one perfume and one compact bear delicately adorned with golden vintage trims. The heads are removable. $350.00 for the pair. Private Collection.

**PLATE 322**
Bears drinking beer? The 2" (5 cm) synthetic suede Teddy in lederhosen prefers sipping his from a silver stein. $125.00. Two tinier companions ½" (1 cm) to ⅝" (1.5 cm) have crawled into their vintage mug and refuse to leave. $100.00 each. All three were meticulously sewn by artist Sandy Williams. The ¾" (2 cm) brown bear at right has been hugged once too often (or had one too many?) and was crocheted by Maggie Anderson. $20.00.

**PLATE 323**
Hopping and bopping, this 2¼" (5.5 cm) 1950's style bear
by April Whitcomb Gustafson wears a swinging pink
skirt with a Polar bear applique. No poodles, please.
April made this Teddy to coordinate with her own outfit
for the "Blast to the Past" party at Disneyland's first bear
convention. $325.00.

**PLATE 324**
Clothes often add to the character of a bear. This white cro-
cheted cap, gown, and booties (by June Chapman) give Lisa
Lloyd's 2½" (6.5 cm) tan bear an innocent, little girl look.
$150.00. Private Collection.

**PLATE 325**
Durae Allen is the imaginative creator of this itsy-bitsy, teeny-weeny bear in red polka-dot
bikini. The 2¾" (7 cm) plush Teddy's outfit is completely coordinated right down to the
matching red bows on her custom beach sandals. $100.00. Private Collection.

135

**PLATE 326**
These 3" (7.5 cm) Teds by Odette Conley come costumed in pink or blue cotton dresses, black patent leather shoes, and straw summer hats. Each Teddy girl carries her own beloved black doll. $140.00 each. Courtesy Good Hearted Bears.

**PLATE 327**
Red silk roses adorn the elegant evening gown of this 2" tan Teddy by Julia Watada. Black faceted crystal eyes, a beaded bracelet and earrings, and racy red panties complete the effect. $110.00.

**PLATE 328**
Out for a Sunday stroll, this 2¾" (7 cm) lady bear by Sharon Thompson Soule (with a pom-pom puppy at her side) wears a lace dress, hat, and silk parasol. $75.00. The 1" (2.5 cm) white bear by Kathryn Franze wears a matching lace shawl and straw hat trimmed in blue. $50.00.

**PLATE 329**
"Madam T.R." (right) by Kathryn Franze is only 1½" (4 cm) high with her fancy straw hat and rose pink sweater. $60.00. Her 2⅜" (6 cm) companion, "Heidi Bear," by Julia Watada wears a dress sewn from French ribbon with an overlay bodice of lace. A wreath of silk roses and beads and a small straw basket complete the storybook picture. $110.00.

**PLATE 330**
Ballerina bears in matching pink tutus practice their pirouettes and dance together "en pointe." The 2½" (6.5 cm) dancer at left with a sexy satin bodice and graceful pink toe shoes, is by Kathryn Franze. $75.00. The 1" (2.5 cm) balancing ballerina at center is of ribbon-trimmed Fimo by Karen Gibbs. $25.00. The 3" (7.5 cm) resting bear at right is skillfully machine sewn by Pat Carriker. $45.00.

**PLATE 331**
Janie McQuillan's 2" (5 cm), pert, yellow plush Teddy girl wears a pale blue dress of ruffled ribbon with a matching straw hat. A darling little dog stands loyally by her bear-mistress's side. $85.00.

**PLATE 332**
Janie Comito's 4¼" (11 cm) tan mohair girl bear is elaborately costumed in vintage, Victorian style ribbon and lace. And what girl Teddy would be truly complete without her own tiny dolly-bear? The 2¼" (5.5 cm) tall confection is fancifully clothed from her rose and ribbon-trimmed hat right down to the long lacy bloomers beneath her green taffeta skirt. $450.00 for the pair. Courtesy Karen Thompson.

**PLATE 333**
"Rose" is the perfectly appropriate name Tammie Lawrence gave to her 6" (15 cm) Victorian Teddy creation. Every inch of this frilly, feminine bear is sewn with care and stuffed with personality. The incredibly fancy, frou-frou headpiece is scented with potpourri, an extra, inviting touch to a very tempting Teddy. $275.00.

**PLATE 334**
Elaine Fujita-Gamble's 2¾" (7 cm) lady bear wears a lovely lavender gown of embroidered cotton, with a demure straw hat of deep blue. She travels with her own china tea set and prefers honey over sugar, please. $95.00.

PLATE 335
This classically costumed, 2" (5 cm), cleverly sewn and suited Bellhop Bear by Sandy Williams may have his paws full trying to lift the 1¾" (4.5 cm) black Victorian doll house trunk. Bear, $125.00; trunk, $50.00. "Rosabear" by Kimberlee Port may be easier to deliver. The 1¼" gray plush bear comes in her own red, rose-trimmed, gift box. With Teddies like her who needs flowers? $275.00.

PLATE 336
Kimberlee Port's 2¼" (5.5 cm) "Sugar Ann" is sewn of light tan mohair and costumed in a vintage ribbon-trimmed dress. She carries her own, minuscule bear muff with movable arms and legs and arrives in a lovely box that doubles as her vine-covered cottage. $550.00. Private Collection.

**PLATE 337**
These two Victorian girl bears by Janie Comito, 3" (7.5 cm) and 2¾" (7 cm), are the best of friends. They both wear darling outfits of lace, snippets, ruching, ribbon, and roses. High-button shoes and piquant pantaloons peep from beneath their full, fancy skirts. $250.00 – $385.00 each. Private Collection.

**PLATE 338**
Cynthia Powell's Victorian bear brooch is designed to dress you in high Teddy style. Small scraps of vintage lace and pearl button trims accent the 1¾" (4.5 cm) antique-toned Teddy. $185.00.

**PLATE 339**
A flea-market "find" by Janie Comito, (a vintage straw hat) was recycled into this ravishing, one of a kind creation. The 2¼" (5.5 cm) girl Teddy rests among an old silk rose and a delightful bunch of violets, her costume perfectly coordinated with the flowers and ribbon trim. This delightful idea could be the ultimate excuse for bringing your bear to a picnic or informal afternoon tea. $650.00. Private Collection.

**PLATE 340**
Dancing on top of a pink satin rose is a 2½" (5 cm) ballerina bear by Durae Allen (left) with black glass eyes, a brown floss nose, and matching white hair and ankle bows. $120.00. Accompanying her is a 1¼" (3 cm) white plush, tutu-clad Ted by Lisa Lloyd (right). $150.00. Private Collection.

**PLATE 341**
Janie McQuillan's 2½" (6 cm) lovely yellow "Wee B" bear wears a lace-trimmed cap with pink ribbons gathered at the crown. $55.00. She prepares for bedtime by feeding her pajama-clad, rattle-wielding baby bear, crocheted by Dolores Szuba. $30.00.

**PLATE 342**
This 2" Baby Teddy by Sara Phillips is made of hand-dyed pink mohair with turned-down paws, a velvet-like snout and feet, and an engaging, open mouth. A fabulous, fitting tribute to his antique ancestors (or should I say fore-bears?). $160.00.

**PLATE 343**
Bedtime and bears go together naturally like this 2" (5 cm) girl Teddy by Sara Phillips wearing a custom, panda-print nightgown and cap, coordinating green, bear head slippers, and carrying her own ¾" (2 cm) panda pal. A combination sure to give any Teddy collector sweet dreams. $325.00 for the pair. Private Collection.

**PLATE 344**
Elaine Fujita-Gamble's 2½" Teddy girl is ready to take her own 1" (2.5 cm) bear to bed. Her pink cotton nightgown, delicately trimmed with tatting, was designed from a vintage handkerchief and the extra-fuzzy bunny slippers will surely keep her feet warm. $175.00 together.

**PLATE 345**
It's dress-up time for these two boy bears imitating their favorite patriotic figures. Laurie Sasaki's 1¾" (4.5 cm) "Yankee Doodle Teddy" wears a blue, star-spangled, sailor shirt, a cap of folded newsprint, and a make-shift wooden sword while riding his painted stick pony. $175.00. Kathryn Franze's 1½" (4 cm) "T.R." sports a rough rider style hat and monocle astride his 1½" (4 cm) Horsie on Wheels. $100.00 for bear and horse pair.

**PLATE 346**
Dickie Harrison's 3¼" (8 cm) "Teddy B and Teddy G" were creatively costumed and cleverly reproduced from the cover of Seymour Eaton's early 1900's book, *The Roosevelt Bears.* "Baby Teddy B," a 1⅝" (4 cm) version, stands by their side. $300.00 for the set.

PLATE 348
Sara Phillips designed these two "Treasure Bears" as the "Rose Diamond Queen and Blue Sapphire King," carefully guarding their royal riches. The 2½" (6.5 cm) seated bears have bodies made of hollow walnuts, which open to show tummies lined in 24 karat gold leaf, filled with specially selected vintage charms. $160.00 each.

PLATE 347
These two Teddies are real examples of bear royalty. The 3¼" (8 cm) "Mini Bear King" by Durae Allen wears a rich red cape, golden sword and shield, and a jewel-encrusted crown. $120.00. The 2½" (6.5 cm) Ted of princely-appearance (right), by Howard and Karen Calvin, wears a lace ruff, a tiny crown encircled with pearls, and a two-tone, gold-trimmed costume. $120.00. Courtesy Karen Thompson.

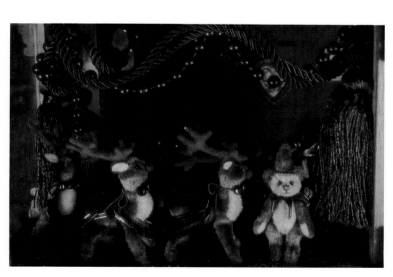

PLATE 349
Miniature displays allow some collectors to enjoy the holidays year round. A 1¾" (4.5 cm) green panda elf leads a group of plush reindeer in this Christmastime window designed by Cynthia Powell. $800.00 for the four piece set. Private Collection.

PLATE 350
This 1¾" (4.5 cm) cream plush bear by Cynthia Powell is covered with ⅝" (1.5 cm) multi-colored cubs. Each tiny Ted is individually sewn of synthetic suede and the pink porcelain shoe seemed to perfectly "fit" their situation. $975.00 complete. Private Collection.

**PLATE 351**
Sandy Williams decorated this scrumptious pink heart-shaped candy box with flowers, French ribbons, and pearls then created two coordinating Teddies to fit inside. "Rose" is a 1¾" (4.5 cm) bear of tan plush, deliciously dressed in pearls and lace, and carries her ⅝" (1.5 cm) dolly bear of mauve and cream synthetic suede. A cute, calorie-free Valentine treat. $325.00.

**PLATE 352**
Boo! This 1¾" (4.5 cm) orange mohair bear by Sara Phillips is "Oh! So, Scary!" in his spider-web lace collar (complete with spider) and swivel head that displays a Jack-o-lantern smile on the other side. He's shown riding a 2" (5 cm), c. 1920's fuzzy black cat with a 1" (2.5 cm) vintage plastic cat by his side. Bear, $175.00; cats, $20.00 – $135.00.

**PLATE 353**
Barbara Conley's 5" (12.5 cm) acrylic Teddy wears a bright coat of Christmas red, tan felt pads, a brown floss nose, and black glass "adopt me" eyes. $195.00. Courtesy Amanda Prugh.

**PLATE 354**
Dressed for the holidays in their colorful costumes are a 3¼" (8 cm) Nutcracker and 2½" (6.5 cm) Snowshoe Santa by Laurie Sasaki. These beautiful bears show amazing attention to detail from the Nutcracker's embroidered and painted coat and cap to the toy-filled pack on Santa's back. $250.00 – $275.00 each.

**PLATE 355**
This fancy Valentine Teddy by Sara Phillips would be a loveable treat for any collector. She is 1½"
(4 cm) high, clad in a floral hat and red velvet cape and clutches a coordinating bear-head muff
(heart-shaped, of course!) $175.00. Private Collection.

**PLATE 356**
Standing on a white snowflake base, these blustery bear buddies by Elaine Fujita-Gamble build a statue in the snow (possibly a snow-bear?). The 3" (7.5 cm) plush Teddy in a red and brown-trimmed coat wears pants and mittens in Christmas green. The 1¾" (4.5 cm) bear keeps warm beneath his built-in tan "coat" and woolen scarf. $160.00 for the set.

**PLATE 357**
Carol Stewart's 2¾" (7 cm) "Narley" of white curly cotton, wears a hand-knit holiday sweater and cap by Mary Koshuta and silver glasses that give him a wise, wintry look. $200.00.

**PLATE 358**
Brenda Dewey's 6" (15 cm) Jack-o-lantern jester wears a creative costume of pumpkin orange and vine green with a spooky black mask and carved-out jingle bell. Curly green tendrils and leaves escaping from his hat and collar add an extra fall-time flair. $125.00. Private Collection.

**PLATE 359**
Beth Hogan's 3" (7.5 cm) Black Cat bear wears a custom-fitted kitty cap, black "cat-suit," and carries his own toy mouse (hand-stitched in white synthetic suede). A "purr-fect" Halloween treat. $95.00. Courtesy Karen Thompson.

**PLATE 360**
This 2⅝" (6.5 cm) Easter Bunny Bear by Julia Watada comes with long, ravishing rabbit-ears and a papier-maché egg for a great hiding place. Teddy is sewn of egg-shell plush, with synthetic suede paw pads, silk roses, ribbons and black bead eyes. $110.00.

**PLATE 361**
Cindy Martin's 4" (10 cm) "Tiny Clown Yesterbear" wears a ruff and ribbon-trimmed suit of pale green mohair with a white head, paws, and feet, and pink suede pads. The enchanting "Cindy-style" expression was achieved through a combination of needle-sculpting and antique silk embroidery. This is Cindy's own Teddy, one of two, which sits in a green wicker doll's chair, c. 1900. Bear, $350.00; chair, $75.00.

**PLATE 362**
Clown bears have been a favorite theme of Teddy-makers since the early bear craze began. Carol Stewart's 2¼" (5.5 cm) tan plush drummer comes with a colorful pom-pom hat, red ruff, and a matching miniature drum. $160.00.

**PLATE 363**
This circus set was sold in the early 1980's as a signed, limited edition from Kathryn Franze. The 1¼" (3 cm) tan clown Ted wears a white ruff and pointed, polka-dot hat into the ring on his 2" (5 cm) gray elephant on wheels. $125.00 for the set.

**PLATE 364**
Cathy Levy's 1¾" (4.5 cm) Jack-in-the-box wears a vivid purple hat and rose-trimmed ribbon ruff made to match his red, white, and green octagonal box. $160.00. A 2¼" (5.5 cm) brown basic bear with contrasting color muzzle and paws sits patiently at his side (waiting for "Jack" to jump?). $135.00. Courtesy Karen Thompson.

**PLATE 365**
Dickie Harrison's 3½" (9 cm) jaunty Jester wears a red and green Christmas costume and carries a tiny teddy-head poupard. This two-Teddy set would make any collector's holidays happy. $110.00.

**PLATE 366**
Kim Port's 2¾" (7 cm) "Clown T. Bear" and 3" (7.5 cm) long "Turn Head Jester" were sold as a set, beautifully boxed in a color coordinated hand-made container. The red riding bear contains a hidden "no-no" tail mechanism and his gray clown companion comes fully jointed. $875.00 together. Private Collection.

**PLATE 367**
A bit of wide-eyed whimsy is captured in the face and costume of this 3" (7.5 cm) clown by Durae Allen. The yellow and red polka-dot pants with patches, iridescent rainbow bow-tie, black, oversized shoes, and bright orange nose simply invite a laugh or smile. $125.00. Private Collection.

**PLATE 368**
The 5½" (14 cm) lace-collared clown by Howard and Karen Calvin, bounces a 1¾" (4.5 cm) tan basic bear on his knee. The vividly costumed clown has a highly stylized body shape with long curved arms, super-skinny ankles, and funny, oversized feet. The extra-wide Calvin smile has a contagious effect on collectors. Jester, $150.00; small Ted, $120.00. Courtesy Karen Thompson.

**PLATE 369**
Pink and green plush with a lacy pink ruff and matching poupard give this 3" (7.5 cm) jester by Cathy Levy a vintage, Victorian look. Dark, shaded glass eyes and a bi-color embroidered nose add individuality to an unforgettable face. $250.00. Private Collection.

**PLATE 370**
An expressive open mouth and carnival style costume give the 1½" (4 cm) panda clown by Sara Phillips (left) a fun, festive look. A tiny panda puppet accompanies this Ted on all of his routines. $175.00. Julia Watada's fuzzy white jester bear (right) measures 1¾" (4.5 cm) from the bottom of his maroon and blue feet to the top of his double-pointed hat. Vintage trims and a matching poupard add to the old world effect. $120.00.

**PLATE 371**
Laurie Sasaki's 2" (5 cm) colorful clown Teddy wears a two-tone synthetic suede outfit with a double row of silk ruffles and star-backed buttons. $150.00.

**PLATE 372**
"Emmet and Friend" by Gail Silversmith are the first edition of a delightful clown set designed especially for this book. The 3¼" (8 cm) and 2⅜" (6 cm) pair was sewn from hand-dyed synthetic plush and trimmed with gilded organdy, rhinestones, and golden cording. $275.00 for the set.

**PLATE 373**
A 3" (7.5 cm) clown and 2¼" (5.5 cm) jester by Lisa Lloyd escape from the circus to pose for their picture. Neon-bright costumes, heavily spangled with ribbons and beads distinguish these two show-stoppers. $110.00 – $140.00 each.

**PLATE 374**
Durae Allen's 2½" Bumble bear buzzes by a daffodil bouquet in his search for (you guessed it) honey! Sheer, shimmering wings and pearly white antennae are a subtle contrast to his bright yellow, bee-utiful coat. $125.00. Private Collection.

**PLATE 375**
A 2¾" (7 cm) wooden acorn is home to a 1½" (4 cm) mushroom sprite by Sara Phillips. This wonderful, woodland bear has a red mushroom cap with antennae, velvet leaf "wings," and a tiny red lady-bug, which has landed on his leg. The acorn itself is also adorned with golden charms and mushroom trims. $160.00.

**PLATE 376**
Beth Hogan's 3¼" (8 cm) rose-toned flower fairy bear wears elaborate lace wings softly-studded with rhinestones, a crystal wand (to bestow miniature bear magic), green antennae, and a hand-sculpted ladybug (for luck). Pellet stuffing makes this bear particularly poseable. $135.00. Courtesy Karen Thompson.

**PLATE 377**
According to artist Janie Comito, bears have the nesting instinct, too. This 2½" (6 cm) winged spring Teddy snuggles in a sweet-smelling bed of potpourri. $300.00.

**PLATE 378**
Wild and wonderful is the only way to describe this huggable, hot pink bear by Beth Hogan. A same-colored synthetic suede snout and black nose, eyes, claws, and ribbon ruff set the fancy color off to perfection. $85.00. Private Collection.

**PLATE 379**
Howard and Karen Calvin created this 2" (5 cm) fuschia flutterbear with iridescent orange wings. The fun, fantasy-type Teddy comes with white antennae and a cord for "flying" him by. $135.00. Private Collection.

**PLATE 380**
A true Teddy fantasy, Laurie Sasaki's 2" (5 cm) plush and synthetic suede elfin bear, harnesses butterfly power to sail the skies and collect spring flowers in the straw basket on his back. $250.00.

# Chapter Ten

# The Smallest Bear in the World

After seeing so many marvelous miniatures, you may have a hard time choosing a favorite. In this last chapter we will not try to select the best, but merely the ittiest, bittiest bear. So which Teddy is truly the smallest? Many artists and manufacturers may claim that their baby bruin is indeed the teeniest weeniest Teddy. But can this conclusion be reached by sheer measurement alone? Certainly not! Other criteria must be considered. Should the bear be sewn by hand or carved in clay? Can he be poured in plastic or porcelain, or perhaps whittled out of wood? Jointed or unjointed? Standing or sitting? Fluffed, buffed or stuffed? Who can say? You, of course, by viewing the following photos and cheering for the candidate of your choice. Ultimately, it is up to the collector to decide which is the smallest true Teddy Bear.

**PLATE 382**
**Two more candidates for smallest Ted are the ½" (1 cm) fully jointed, multi-colored patchwork cub in synthetic suede by Cynthia Powell, and a ¼" (½ cm) baby bear bundled in his own cradle. $155.00.**

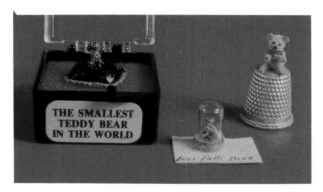

**PLATE 381**
**Will the smallest Teddy please stand up? These three, all under ¼" (.75 cm), are: at left, by Menteith Miniatures of Scotland, a c. 1980's 22k gold-plated pewter bear, (no longer produced), sitting on his own hand-enameled blue pillow in a very official-looking box (perfect for proving to friends that you own the ultimate in bitty bruins). At center, by Jill Hague, is "Wee Patty Bear" an Irish-type Teddy of Fimo clutching a tiny clover, encased in his own glass dome. At right is a petite bear made from pom-poms, possibly the smallest fuzzy bear? $15.00 – $35.00 each.**

**PLATE 383**
**Maggie Anderson made the ¾" (2 cm) colorful crochet bear (top left), and Louisa Padilla of Under the Hedgerow produced the ½" (1 cm) dressed porcelain pair. John Giles of Sedona, AZ sculpted and skillfully painted the ⅝" (1.5 cm) sleeping bear (lower left). The two synthetic suede bears (lower right) were hand sewn by Rose Policky (½"/1 cm caramel bear) and Sandy Williams (⅝"/1.5 cm off-white Teddy). $20.00 – $100.00 each.**

**PLATE 384**
The blossoms are all a-buzz with these ⅝" (1.5 cm) bumble-bears by Julia Watada. Each hand-stitched Teddy-bee comes in his own silk flower bouquet. $100.00 each.

**PLATE 385**
Other amazing, near microscopic Teddies include the 1" (2.5 cm) wooden bear-maker's stall by Susan Kruger (top), a ¾" (2 cm) tan-colored king and pink clay bear by Dewitt Boyd, and a ¾" (2 cm) fimo peddlar Teddy by Karen Gibbs holding a tray of minuscule bear marvels. $12.00 – $75.00 each.

**PLATE 386**
Jill Hague made the ½" (1 cm) Baby Buggy bear (holding her own baby bear) (top left), Karen Gibbs sculpted the ¾" (2 cm) mother with baby in blanket, and Maggie Anderson crafted the ¾" (2 cm) brown boy bear in green P.J.'s holding a smaller pink bedtime buddy. $15.00 – $25.00 each.

**PLATE 387**
¾" (2 cm) Czechoslovakian glass bears (and other animals) like the metal-collared one with rhinestone eyes (right) were manufactured from the 1920's, possibly to imitate the Fabergé-made crystal animals of the previous decade. The two at left are difficult to date and could be more contemporary versions. $10.00 – $30.00 each.

**PLATE 388**
A ¾" (2 cm) painted metal panda (British) from the early 1980's and a ¾" (2 cm) music box bear by Karen Gibbs pose patiently on silk-covered spools. $15.00 – $20.00 each.

**PLATE 389**
"The Smallest Bear in The World," c. 1920's, came complete with a blue celluloid cradle and 1" (2.5 cm) cream cardboard box proclaiming its small bear superiority. The ⅝" (1.5 cm) light brown standing bruin-type Ted was surely the tiniest made at the time. $200.00 up. Private Collection.

**PLATE 390**
The ½" (1.25 cm) ballerina bear (center) was crocheted by Margaret Crossland, and the ¼" (.75 cm) porcelain basic bear at bottom right was produced by Louisa Padilla. John Giles may have made the Teddy to top them all, at ⅛" (.5 cm) the beautifully detailed bear is of handpainted clay, and dainty enough to dance on the head of a pin. $10.00 – $15.00.

# Bibliography

**Books:**

Brewer, Kim and Carol-Lynn Rössel Waugh. *The Official Price Guide to Antique and Modern Teddy Bears.* New York: The House of Collectibles, Random House, 1990.

Cieslik, Jürgen and Marianne. *Button in Ear.* West Germany: Marianne Cieslik Verlag, 1989.

Huber, Rudger. *Schuco.* Germany: Battenberg Verlag Augsburg, 1991.

Mandel, Margaret Fox. *Teddy Bears, Annalee's and Steiff Animals.* Paducah, KY: Collector Books, 1990.

Mullins, Linda. *Teddy Bears Past and Present.* Cumberland, MD: Hobby House Press, Inc., 1991.

Pistorius, Rolf and Christel. *Steiff, Sensational Teddy Bears, Animals and Dolls.* Cumberland, MD: Hobby House Press, Inc., 1991.

Schoonmaker, Patricia N. *A Collector's History of the Teddy Bear.* Cumberland, MD: Hobby House Press, Inc., 1981.

Wilson, Jean. *Steiff Toys Revisited.* Radnor, PA: Wallace Homestead Book Company, 1989.

Wyler, Seymour B. *The Book of Old Silver.* New York: Crown Publishers, Inc., 1937.

**Articles:**

Ackerman, Evelyn. "Schuco's Other Miniature Animals." *The Teddy Bear and Friends.* Hobby House Press, Spring 1985, pages 26-30.

Ackerman, Evelyn. "Schuco's Miniature Teddy Bears." *The Teddy Bear and Friends.* Summer 1983, pages 29-31.

Jennings, Richard. "Titanic Teddy." *Teddy Bear Times.* Ashdown Publishing, Spring 1992, pages 40-41.

Hamilton, Elizabeth Bentley. "Further Notes on Schuco's Miniature Teddy Bears." *The Teddy Bear and Friends.* Winter 1938/84, pages 18-19.

Leistner, Erich. "The History of the Schuco Miniature Tin Bears." *The Teddy Bear and Friends.* June 1987, pages 46-51.

**Catalogs:**

Schuco's 25th Anniversay Catalog, Schreyer and Co., 1937.

Schuco's 50th Anniversay Catalog, Schreyer and Co., 1962.

# Resource Guide

An excellent place to begin your Teddy treasure hunt is between the covers of a bear magazine. Shops, shows, artists, collectors and dealers can all be found within their pages. If you are at all interesed in starting or expanding your collection, subscriptions to one or more of these is a must:

*The Teddy Bear and Friends*
(from Cumberland Publishing, Inc.)
900 Frederick Street
Cumberland, MD 21502

*Teddy Bear Review*
(from Collector Communications Corp.)
170 Fifth Ave.
New York, N.Y. 10010

*Teddy Bear Times*
(from Ashdown Publishing) U.S. Office:
Heritage Press
3150 State Line Road
Cincinnati, North Bend, Ohio, 45052

Many retail shops and antique dealers across the country sell fine Teddies and collectibles. The best way to buy a bear from these specialists is in person, when you can carefully inspect your purchase on the spot. The most tantalizing Teddies, however, are not always found close to home, so many shops and dealers are willing to sell on approval. As with any important purchases in your life, protect yourself with knowledge.

Following are just a few of the folks who carry miniature Teds on a regular basis:

### Shops:

The Owl and The Pussycat
15200 U.S. 41 South
Ft. Myers, FL 33908
(813)-489-4354

Good Hearted Bears
½ Pearl Street
Mystic, CT 06355
(203)-536-2468

The Calico Teddy
22 E. 24th Street
Baltimore, MD 21218
(410)-889-4722

Groves Quality Collectibles
349 S. Jameson Avenue
Lima, Ohio, 45805
(419)-229-7177

*The following dealers sell mainly at shows, or by mail order:*

Michelle Daunton
288 Mohawk Trail
Bridgewater, N.J. 08807
(908)-526-7657

David Douglass
Antique Bears
88 Alpine Trail
Sparta, N.J. 07871
(201)-729-3633

Barbara Lauver
Harper General Store
R.D. #2, Box 512
Annville, PA 17003
(717)-865-3456

Nancy Torode
Ice Pond Antiques
Acton, MA 01720
(508)-263-8078

Domenico Idoni
Box 247
Greenwood, MD 21738
(301)-916-1311

Barbara and Byron Baldwin
Old Friends Antiques
P.O. Box 754
Sparks, MD 21152
(410)-472-4632

Harriet Purtill, Antiques
127 Neipsic Road
Glastonbury, CT 06033
(203)-633-1784

Donna Harrison West
(410)-544-4526
(carries antique and collectible Teddies and promotes a bi-annual east coast show)

***In England, try:***

Bears and Friends of Brighton
32 Meeting House Lane
The Lanes, Brighton, BN1 1HB England
Phone — 0273-208940

Teddy Bears
99 High Street
Witney, Oxfordshire, OX8 6LY
Phone — 0993 702616

Wendy Lewis
Unique of Broadway
76 High Street
Broadway, Cotswolds, Worcs WR12 7AJ
Phone — 0386 858323

Sue Pearson
13½ Prince Albert Street
The Lanes, Brigton-Sussex
Phone — 0273-29247

Pam Hebbs
5 The Annexe
Camden Passage
Islington, London N1
(081)-361-3739

Peter and Frances Fagan
Colour Box
Orchard Estate, Lauder
Berwickshire, Scotland TD2 GRH

Another way to network with miniature bear makers and collectors is through an international organization appropriately named S.M.A.L.L. Founded by an enthusiastic bear-maker and collector, Deanne Crim, in 1990, this fun group "is set up to be a forum for selling, trading, collecting, and friendship making with a mail and telephone basis." A bi-monthly newsletter, "Bearmail Convention," and annual tea-party are just a few of the opportunities offered to its many members. For information on joining, write to: Deanne Crim, S.M.A.L.L. Headquarters, 951 S. Copper Key Court, Gilbert, AZ 85234.